THE POWER
OF POETRY

HOPE · THE FUTURE · EQUALITY · POVERTY · WAR · DISASTER · DESTRUCTION · DISCRIMINATION · BULLYING · POLLUTION · IDENTITY · POWER

# Set Your Voices Free

Edited By Jenni Harrison

First published in Great Britain in 2023 by:

 Young**Writers**

Young Writers
Remus House
Coltsfoot Drive
Peterborough
PE2 9BF
Telephone: 01733 890066
Website: www.youngwriters.co.uk

Printed and bound in the UK by BookPrintingUK
Website: www.bookprintinguk.com
YB0528T

# FOREWORD

Since 1991, here at Young Writers we have celebrated the awesome power of creative writing, especially in young adults where it can serve as a vital method of expressing their emotions and views about the world around them. In every poem we see the effort and thought that each student published in this book has put into their work and by creating this anthology we hope to encourage them further with the ultimate goal of sparking a life-long love of writing.

Our latest competition for secondary school students, **The Power of Poetry,** challenged young writers to consider what was important to them and how to express that using the power of words. We wanted to give them a voice, the chance to express themselves freely and honestly, something which is so important for these young adults to feel confident and listened to. They could give an opinion, highlight an issue, consider a dilemma, impart advice or simply write about something they love. There were no restrictions on style or subject so you will find an anthology brimming with a variety of poetic styles and topics. We hope you find it as absorbing as we have.

We encourage young writers to express themselves and address subjects that matter to them, which sometimes means writing about sensitive or contentious topics. If you have been affected by any issues raised in this book, details on where to find help can be found at
**www.youngwriters.co.uk/info/other/contact-lines**

# CONTENTS

## All Saints Catholic College, London

## Ark Greenwich Free School, Woolwich

## Broomfield School, Southgate

## Cramlington Learning Village, Cramlington

## Edgbarrow School, Crowthorne

## Greenfield Community College, Newton Aycliffe

| | |
|---|---|
| Reece Preston (13) | 66 |
| James Dean (11) | 68 |
| Owain McTighe (15) | 69 |
| Isach Moore (14) | 70 |

## Jordanhill School, Glasgow

| | |
|---|---|
| Ethan Jiang (11) | 71 |
| Ewan Pilsworth (13) | 72 |
| Ryan Roy (12) | 74 |
| Leila Rowe (12) | 75 |
| Calum Anderson (12) | 76 |
| Lily Weir (11) | 78 |
| Krishna Vundavalli (11) | 79 |
| Charlotte Teece (12) | 80 |
| Hannah Kainth (12) | 81 |
| Tom Sloane (12) | 82 |
| Andrew Black (12) | 83 |
| Millie Johnstone (12) | 84 |
| James Lowdon (12) | 85 |
| Ellie Johnstone (12) | 86 |
| Jessica Doran (13) | 87 |
| Euan Palmer (12) | 88 |
| Joel McEwan (12) | 89 |
| Ethan McLean (12) | 90 |

## King Edward VI Handsworth Wood Girls' Academy, Birmingham

| | |
|---|---|
| Elilta Angosom (11) | 91 |
| Fatimah Bibi (11) | 92 |
| Ubaydah Adenuga (11) | 94 |
| Imaan Ishtiaq (12) | 95 |
| Parmeet Kaur (12) | 96 |
| Saimah Yasmin (11) | 97 |
| Aliza Rafaqat (12) | 98 |
| Aanya Kochhar (11) | 99 |
| Inayah Begum (11) | 100 |
| Ronika Taghizadeh (11) | 101 |
| Eliza Salam (12) | 102 |

| | |
|---|---|
| Safah Hussain (11) | 103 |
| Gurleen Kaur (11) | 104 |
| Ruqyyah Fatima (12) | 105 |

## Marden High School, North Shields

| | |
|---|---|
| Charlie Colaco (13) | 106 |
| Aaron Richardson (12) | 108 |
| Gabriel Kennedy (12) | 109 |
| Lucy Turner (13) | 110 |
| Hazell Oliver (14) | 111 |
| Katie McLeod (12) | 112 |
| Toby Todd (12) | 113 |

## Pearson Online Academy, London

| | |
|---|---|
| Aizah Undre (14) | 114 |
| Aasiyah Khimji (17) | 116 |
| Alyssa Springer-Cupid (16) | 118 |
| Emily Oldman (14) | 119 |

## Poltair School, St Austell

| | |
|---|---|
| Myya Johns (11) | 120 |
| Ella Brooks-Richardson (16) | 122 |

## Reddam House Berkshire, Wokingham

| | |
|---|---|
| Kara Crawford-McLeod (12) | 123 |
| Dare Cross (12) | 124 |
| Danny Royle (12) | 127 |
| Poppy McManus-Smith (12) | 128 |
| Sami Syed (11) | 131 |
| Zara Bates (12) | 132 |
| Carla Cuadrado Barrero (11) | 134 |
| Jerry Xie (12) | 136 |
| Gwyneth Thornton (11) | 138 |
| Elliot Stirling (12) | 140 |
| Cedric Ma (12) | 142 |
| Darcilia Zhong (12) | 144 |
| Vismay Ganesh (12) | 146 |
| Seth Sandhu (12) | 148 |
| Ariella Avidi (11) | 149 |

| Ava Dowding (12) | 150 |
|---|---|
| Sophie Noone (12) | 151 |
| Florence Slater (12) | 152 |
| Chloe Dell (12) | 153 |
| Erin Sandhu (11) | 154 |
| Romilly Haworth (13) | 155 |
| Timi Owolabi (12) | 156 |
| Millie Khin (13) | 157 |
| Sully Palmer (12) | 158 |
| Daniel Slade (12) | 159 |
| India Nicholls (11) | 160 |
| Henry Hallett (13) | 161 |
| Joyce Lo (11) | 162 |
| Francesca McLoughlin (13) | 163 |
| Friedman Lo | 164 |
| Phoebe Ayton-Judd (11) | 165 |
| Artemis Kompocholi (11) | 166 |
| Sienna Pugh (11) | 167 |
| Emilio Aspin (11) | 168 |

## Solihull Sixth Form College, Solihull

| Yaynah Welsh (17) | 169 |
|---|---|
| Amber Ewins (16) | 170 |
| Nel Kabenga (16) | 172 |
| Emily Lander (16) | 173 |
| Leah Berry (16) | 174 |
| Isabela Sopawiro (16) | 176 |
| Kleio Wardle (16) | 177 |
| Marcie Allen (17) | 178 |
| Safa Abdi (16) | 179 |
| Sheree Wyatt (16) | 180 |
| Hannah Moloney (17) | 181 |
| Fiona Higgins | 182 |
| Robbie English (16) | 183 |
| Macey Ward (16) | 184 |

## Tiree High School, Isle Of Tiree

| Eddie Maclean (12) | 185 |
|---|---|
| Casey Colthart (13) | 186 |
| Anya Wright (12) | 189 |
| Aidan Hynes (11) | 190 |

| Charlotte Vale (12) | 191 |
|---|---|
| Zoe Maguire (12) | 192 |
| Iona MacDonald (11) | 193 |
| Molly Knowles (14) | 194 |
| Evie Meyer (12) | 195 |
| Lewis Gunn (13) | 196 |
| Honey-Jane Romio (13) | 197 |
| Lucy Kennedy (11) | 198 |
| Max MacKinnon (14) | 199 |
| Maurice Wright (11) | 200 |

## Wayland Academy, Watton

| Yuri Silva (11) | 201 |
|---|---|
| Nadia Lenartowicz (11) | 202 |
| Ryan Blockwell (11) | 203 |

# THE
# POEMS

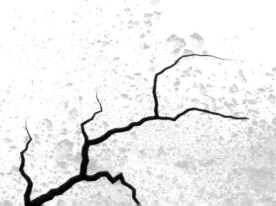

# The World

Animals are dying, begging for their lives,
While all we can do is watch humanity rise.

While trees are desperately waiting for water,
We just stand there and continue with our slaughter.

When they finally rest, thinking safety is found
We start a fire and burn them to the ground.

Chopping them down, one by one,
thinking it's fun,
however, we don't seem to like it
when Mother Nature holds the gun.

Our survival depends on her,
but we don't seem to care,
even though she can send us into years of despair.

You see, she is powerful in every way,
She can kill us any day,
Take the hurricane in Florida or the earthquakes in Japan
but after all this, we still don't understand
that compared to this planet
we are just little grains of sand.

## Matteo Stablum Arseni (12)
All Saints Catholic College, London

# It Pulls The Strings And Makes Them Ring

It pulls the strings and makes them ring
Six, I awaken. "I'm tired."
The strings pull me up to heaven, my wings start to spread.
A second passes as I leave the gates of grass.
But it fades, fades, fades.
The gates of hell shout a nostalgic, familiar *roar, roar.*
The rain pours, pours... every day was such a chore.
Fallen angels across the street with broken wings and
dented strings.
The hand above the sky that had mocked them,
in every day they tell lies of false hopes, hopes, hopes.
Was it love? Was it a lie?
At this point, I couldn't afford to care anymore.
The light side of the dark was always consequential.
People used to fly high in dazing skies.
"Used to." "Used to."
Oh why, oh why must there be strings?
The angel's phone rang and rang and rang.
But nobody came.
Today was a different day, a story I tell,
before I am reduced in the gates of hell.
The work was done, the pain had barely left.
But in my presence was a young, singing dove.
It flew around the sad skies; it sang and sang, bringing small
smiles.

I carefully looked at the wings the dove held up all on its own, with no dented strings.
I had reluctantly smiled, as it flew past me,
I was able to closely see its untouched, virgin wings.
But as I looked above, I was reminded of my strings implanted on my body, the mocking hand had left my soul.
I had a small spark of hope, the dove and I had started to live "the dream"
...But it was now time to wake up.
The dove's holy singing had vanished.
The mocking, controlling hand had grabbed the white dove.
The singing of the dove became thinner and thinner.
The dove's entire body had been crushed into a smaller size, with its once beautiful sparkling eyes starting to become red with torture.
The singing had stopped,
darkness had consumed the small light once again.
The dove fell, lifeless.
Its broken wings had started to fall from it, its virgin wings had now been painted with scars.
The white, heavenly feathers had now been stained with its pure blood.
Its vessel had now been filled with a spirit of eternal void.
The fallen dove had risen, strings had started to fall above the dove as it started to be pierced with the string's small spears.
It had penetrated its eyes and neck like a fish on a hook.
My smile had long ago left my depressing face.

I left as the torturous transformation had begun to operate on the next fallen angel.
Today was a different day.
I was called in for a promotion.
May I fly again?
May my smile come back with something just as pleasing?
Instead, I was presented with a locked room.
In front of me was the mocking, controlling, omniscient hand that presented me with a raging gesture.
It ran up to me, the fearing hand had grabbed my head in a similar way it had grabbed the free dove.
It had forced my head into a pool of darkness, my breath had started to become thinner and thinner.
The remaining liveliness that I had in my spirit had left my body.
Then, silence.
Suddenly, everything that had become of today, started to leave my mind.
I had forgotten my smile.
I had forgotten the dove.
I had forgotten its majestic smile.
I had forgotten its enduring torture.
Silence floods the night...
Six, I awaken. "I'm tired."

## Habi E (15)
All Saints Catholic College, London

# The First Time It Rained

The sky is crying!
Are we all dying?
Is this a gift from the heavens above,
Or a wicked curse to end all love?

Quick, run, take cover,
This may be a spy undercover!
Drops of water are dancing away,
Whilst dropping all around the highway.

The sky is roaring in pain,
Over and over and over again!
The wind is blowing,
As the leaves are flowing.

May this be the end of us all,
When we are all this is definitely something we shall recall.
Puddles of water are forming on the ground,
There's simply so way to avoid them,
They're all around!

Oh wait, stop!
I can't feel another drop,
The sky's tantrum is over,
We're as lucky as a four-leafed clover.

Now I'm sitting at home, thinking and sighing,
"Why was the sky crying?"

**Gabriela Z (11)**
All Saints Catholic College, London

# The Power Of The Immense Evidence

Many people do not understand the power of silence.
It is unsettling and unjust like the deluges of the sky.
People go around with their imagination
but never would depict that the horror of humanity would
be from our manufactured resources.
All the chattering and blabbering confuses my mind
on whether we should speak up or be restricted to the core
of our wills.
The phones we hold are like evidence which speaks our
generation's mind. The sticky notes many people hold to
alert people for help.

Our silence does not help but intensifies the limit on what is
acceptable or not.
Our words are the key to making people happy, not to
imprison them in a dystopic reality.
Our world should be satisfied with its nature and not dismal.
Our future constantly relies on our phones to tell us
but we as humans are the mind of this world
and a greater part of the population.
Our phones are normally used to show rather than protect.
Our voices and actions can make a difference to our world.
Words are liberality.
If the world were bleak with imagination, we would not
survive.

Insanely, without compassion we would all be in immense conflict.
Conflict cannot be stopped with our cameras but with our voices and hands.
We should stop to help rather than videoing a 'viral' video for views
and an increase in popularity status and sociality.
To be stronger, we must acknowledge the bad and greater good humanity of our consciences.
Our mistakes are here to help us learn
but not to continue a decade of horror.
The world needs us when the Internet is not an option to them.
Our humanity should not turn to dismality.

## Macline G (13)
All Saints Catholic College, London

# War

Nobody knows why,
Nobody knows when,
Nobody knows where and how.
The darkness engulfs you as you run for cover.
The uncontrolled panic is like a demon inside of you
forcing you to break down.
Whistles and explosions worse than thunder,
Causing you to run away in your slumber,
making you a puppet for the amusement of others.

That one guy behind the chair ordering the attacks,
He can only see his soldiers losing themselves in war
As they fight for their dear life and more...

In Heaven or in Hell,
Anything is better than a city of fire,
and an army of men who stole your father.
It started with a slaughter, then a bomb and lack of water,
The demon inside of you once again fighting for control,
This time it left a mark in your soul.
A scar so deep it can only be held...
Until you burst and find yourself in Hell.

Suddenly it all starts rushing back,
Your memory, your past.
So much lost yet so much found,
a single poppy burnt to the ground.

A field of mud and despair,
Painted with blood... they called it warfare.
Every step through the trenches, your heart skips a beat, if
only an invisible shadow could tell you where to sleep

You walk and walk. For a second that contains an eternity
you freeze.
Your rifle is your best friend. There is a man...
Same eyes. Same hair. Same look of despair.
He too holds his rifle with his life,
yet a different uniform glimmers in the light.

Am I really going to kill a man?
Is this what I was meant to do?
My rifle drops, he does not think.
A shot! Cold mud against my skin.
A favour unreturned
A drop of blood on the cold floor.

I am sorry Mum, I said I would come back.
Sincerely your boy,
Please cut me some slack.

## Tommaso Stablum Arseni (12)
All Saints Catholic College, London

# People On The Internet Scare Me

The people on the internet scare me
I could only trust my friends.
People do things which shouldn't be allowed
And this should come to an end.
People act before thinking.
I don't feel safe when speaking to them.
I don't know how they'll react.
Will they shout?
Will they scream?
Or will they do both or something in-between?
I don't feel safe with my sister on the internet.
She's growing up too fast.
People on the internet speed this up
In games which always attract the most fans.
My friends on the internet scare me more.
They also grow up fast.
And I'm being left behind,
I want to grow up as well,
But I can't make up my mind
On whether I want to grow up or not
But there shouldn't be much thought
As I don't want to follow trends on apps
That will just make me want to fit into society

More than I already do.
I'm the last thing that scares me on the internet.
I consider myself a follower.
Not a leader.
I want to be people's friend,
Not their enemy
But people on the internet alter things
and do things that shouldn't be allowed.
I'm not proud of myself
Because I stay silent, but I'm scared.
I'm scared of people on the internet.

## Sheree Leigh Terrado (13)
All Saints Catholic College, London

# Endangered

Tiger, tiger, so bright,
In cages all through the night.
Look at your strength and might,
Look at your paws and bite.

Turtle, turtle, of the sea,
Who do you really want to be?
Are you in cages looking at you and me?
Why don't you go and be free?

Rhino, rhino, your horns have power,
They cut your horns hour by hour.
In cages they don't even give you a shower,
And when you die, you will be weaker than a flower.

Whale, whale, swimming around,
You were lost and now are found.
In the sea all I could hear was your sound,
Now the humans are taking your ground.

Orang, orang, biggest monkey of all,
In weight and height, you are tall.
Still you sit there, doing nothing at all,
There's a time when you're going to fall.

All these creatures might die,
And we don't even see them passing by.
Let's be friendly and say hi!
We're damaging habitats and that's not a lie.

## Artur Gomes Teixeira (11)
All Saints Catholic College, London

# Save Our Planet

Many animals live on Earth,
on land and in the sea,
they are all very free,
just like a tree.

Many animals need saving,
don't be one, be two,
time to do what's right,
do it in the day, not night.

Be the better person you can be,
don't make it worse,
don't make these animals lie in a hearse
don't make these animals suffer a curse.

This is what we need to learn,
it's your turn,
time to save rare species,
we need to do this,

Ask your teacher, Mr, Miss,
why are these animals dying?
Everyone needs to keep trying,
don't give up on Planet Earth.

## Isabella Ramkali (11)
All Saints Catholic College, London

# Fantasy

As you close your eyes, make
a wish, and see if it will
come true. Use your imagination
to transport you to a place
you never knew.

You can create a world, a vision
with no compare. As long as
you have the determination you
will make it there.

Colours, smiles and every comfort
you need, will be there waiting
at the place in-between, your
dreams, goals and greatest desires, enjoy the journey before
it expires.

This is your sign to follow your
heart and never ever stop.
make your wishes, close your
eyes and open up your heart.

## Indiana B (11)
All Saints Catholic College, London

# No More Bullying!

Now I'll tell you the truth,
The truth of it all,
Bullying is everywhere,
Even at the mall.

You can't even guess,
You bullies out there,
The pain and fear,
You give them a scare.
When it's all time for bed,
And time to go pray,
They pray for some sickness,
To be sick every day.

Now why do they pray,
To be sick every day?
Because of you,
And your wicked way.

They don't want to go somewhere,
The place that you are at,
They want to be home,
And not called fat.

I'll end this poem,
By asking you,
Some simple questions,
So listen and review.

## Ana-Lucia S (12)
All Saints Catholic College, London

# One Day

One day, I'll focus on the future,
Maybe.
One day, I'll grow up into the person I dreamed to be,
So many things to do.

What should I choose?
Sports, engineering, so many things to do,
What to choose, what to choose?
Music, art, acting,
So many options to choose from.

Skip school or stay?
Student loans or low-paying jobs?
So many things,
My brain is about to blow.

One day, I'll focus on my future.
I don't know what to choose,
No matter what,
I may lose.

**Marcel K (12)**
All Saints Catholic College, London

# Global Warming

Earth is an ineffable place,
It has many sights to see and many people with glee,
One person may laugh whilst another may cry,

Earth is like a collective,
They hear your cries so try to make you feel delight,
They sense your pain and try to make it go away.

Earth is fair,
One man's misfortune might lead to another man's joy
There is nothing else like Earth, so we must cherish
What we've got.
Without Earth we would rot.

## Dinis Coelho Maltes (13)
All Saints Catholic College, London

# The Celestial Globe

The air infuses its poison into our lungs,
Drying our hearts till it reaches our tongues.

The sun fries our brain,
Only to turn us insane.

Our nostrils decay from oxygen's toxicity,
As it gulps life city by city.

The remaining still waters act like mirrors,
Flooding our thoughts, creating triggers.

The air escapes our lungs with a relief of hope,
Ready to turn this rock into a celestial globe.

**Nada Elsayed (15)**
All Saints Catholic College, London

# Black History Month

Our smiles gone.
Our dignity gone.
Our lives gone.
Flogged 24/7,
No breaks picking cotton,
Every day.
No love from no one,
But we made history.

We fought for our
Rights but lost great sacrifices.
Like Carlota Lucumi but
They made us know for

A movement that everyone will
Remember.
BLM.
People showed up to show
Their love for us.
And that is why October is
Black History Month.

## Alexis B (12)
All Saints Catholic College, London

# The Damaged Soul

A single stroke of light in a war field expands the air
Explosively fast.
A shock wave displaces a soldier in a big blast.
Wasted land that dwells, its curse ever-last.
Never rest still.
A damaged soul unfit for its body.
That no longer belongs to the old.
A source of energy from a unified field returns to its present
to
Learn and evolve.

**Victorio Bringhente (11)**
All Saints Catholic College, London

# There Was A Time

There was a time when nobody was discriminated against,
A time when there was no violence.
That could be now,
If only we tried.

I see people being hurt for who they are and people
Crushing others' dreams.

But now is now and we can't change that,
So we must uprise against all oppression
And show them that
We.
Are.
Amazing.

## Orson S de Melo (11)
All Saints Catholic College, London

# Global Warming

I did it, I did
I jumped
I stepped
right off the world into the
big sun.
Global warming is our
biggest threat but no one
will help us.
No one will fix it,
no one will do it,
because no one gives
a damn.
We need to get together
again and sort
our issues out.
We have 7 years,
till we can't fix it.
So we better hurry
up.

**Mia G (11)**
All Saints Catholic College, London

# Ukraine War

So much lost but so much found,
Homes left, right and centre burnt to the ground.
You know it's real when you hear mothers cry and mourn,
How they say it will all be over by the fiery dawn.
Desiccated are the walls that keep us from evil and insane.
Rest in peace almighty Ukraine.

## Cian O'Rourke (12)
All Saints Catholic College, London

# The Devil's Magnum-Opus

I never knew the tender touch of the gods
Could deceive me so much
Our omnipotent Lord
Our knight in shining armour
Where have you gone?
Have you been lost to that murky fog?
All the martyrs your eyes have witnessed
In your illustrious name
Such an act always made me query religious philosophy

My fall from grace was a cry of desperation
That vulgar nature
Which made me the definition of a satanic voluptuary
Rotten angel that's what I am
My mind dark and twisted
To the point of sociopathy
To the point of utter upmost madness
Elysian angel, that's what you are
Written to perfection like Shakespeare's Ophelia

Intoxicating forbidden fruit
That's what some may characterise me
My arcane nature is hidden behind a mask
A mask I've been forced to bear
My thoughts are nothing if not a labyrinth
Making me Ambrosia

You think to be free is to be feral?
I am to live without depersonalisation
I am to be autonomous, without restraint

And who am I? You might ask
Take thine hand
I will guide you through the fog of your mind
And clear away the storm
Because I am the Devil's magnum-opus
Go on, watch me collapse
Watch me weep
Watch me decompose
That's what you do anyway
'Cause who ever cared for the damned?

## Olivia-Nicole Abraham (15)
Ark Greenwich Free School, Woolwich

# I'm Too Young!

I must have been about ten,
Thinking about when I was gonna use a pen.
I was said to be too young (many times),
But I really didn't understand.

I was called out for not understanding 'stuff',
You can just explain, I mean, what's with the bluff?
People used to talk behind my back,
For not liking the colour black (it was cool)

They thought hanging out with older people is what makes them mature,
I mean I used to hang out with my parents, not with a bunch of 16-year-olds!

They thought having phones was cool,
Oh boy, were they wrong.
We'd be outside till we saw the streetlight,
They were inside gossiping or playing Fortnite.

They thought being old was cool,
And I used to just stick with my needle and wool.

## Pranavvya Rathish (13)
Ark Greenwich Free School, Woolwich

# Sonnets And Strawberry Shortcake

Do you really think you know what love is?
I'd dive into a rose's thorns for his!
But do you know how to properly love you?
I'd like to fall into perfect love please.

Will it take honey so sweet, or a cake?
Maybe my heart, as a treat that is baked!
Maybe an apple, caked with my love's sake.
I'd like to fall into perfect love please.

Perfect is how I'd describe your huge heart.
Stitched to perfection, you make my heart part!
You're my perfect remedy, my sweet heart.
I'd like to fall into perfect love please.

I've prepared some sweet tea, and a foxglove.
Under this light moon, please accept my love.

## Imran Chowdhury (13)
Ark Greenwich Free School, Woolwich

# The Gorgeous And Elegant Juliet Rose

Whose Juliet rose is that? I think I know.
Its owner is quite happy though.
Full of joy like a vivid rainbow,
I watch her laugh. I cry hello.

She gives her Juliet rose a shake,
And laughs until her belly aches.
The only other sound's the brake,
Of distant waves and birds awake.

The Juliet rose is elegant and deep,
But she has promises to keep,
After cake and lots of sleep.
Sweet dreams come to her cheap.

She rises from her gentle bed,
With thoughts of kittens in her head,
She eats her jam with lots of bread.
Ready for the day ahead.

**Alex-Nicole Barry (11)**
Ark Greenwich Free School, Woolwich

# Villains And Heroes

If I am the villain...
Where is my hero?
Villains aren't born,
They are created,
And once I was the hero,
I saved them from being the same as me,
Where is my hero?
Why didn't they save me?
Why am I the villain?

## Honey Stockton (12)
Ark Greenwich Free School, Woolwich

# Monsters

My life is destroyed
my family torn away
and I still hate those monsters to this day.
Die demons who took my niece Nancy away
And they don't cry
no heart
no soul
and I wonder why.

**Lily Paget (11)**
Ark Greenwich Free School, Woolwich

# Rain

*A haiku*

Sad and gloomy sky.
Raindrops meeting my window.
Like tears down my face.

## Maya Csizmadia (11)
Ark Greenwich Free School, Woolwich

# London

Stumbling through the street's rumbling fuze,
With constant flutters of the wind,
I keep swaying with its never-ending gusts of blue,
Numbing bitterness piercing my skin.

Wavering, there is a gentle glow through the dreary clouds,
Similar to the silent thunder of the city's crowd.
Hopping over yesterday's puddles, kicking at lost dimes,
Forming blunt ripples against the murky grime.

Unable to fathom where he's rushing,
I notice a man slipping along the hectic road,
Weaving himself through the pushing,
He vanishes from behind a bus, its colour like a scarlet-red
rose.

Blooming dandelions amongst the dying green,
Meek children picking at them like small thieves.
I swerve along a path; pallid, little leaves-
Roaming by my shoes,
As it follows the faint twittering of a bird,
humming to mellow tunes.

A discreet building cloaked by a slumped chestnut tree;
The Victorian structure and gloomy doors,
Vines leading to the church bells by the cemetery,
I'm drawn to pass by, by the spirits that implore.

Day dissolves into dusk.
And the city has sunk;
Under the sharp yellow street lights,
And the bright shimmer of midnight.
Beyond the stars, lay the quivering in the dark,
Their frail figures tremble and endlessly make remarks.
Whilst the city sleeps,
I watch twilight creep,
My legs falling under the horizon's arc.

Taking another step;
My legs start to fumble,
Holding my breath;
My eyes grow heavy,
Taking a step;
My head twirling - perpetually.
Yet I will forever wander, aimlessly.

I'll roam concealed,
During the day,
Then paint imitations of the city's secrets,
During the night.

## Rosa Toprak (14)
Broomfield School, Southgate

# Yesterday's Tomorrow

Running and running
My heart furiously pounding
Blood rushing to the tips of my fingers
The pulse coming in hot waves
Invisible grains of sand fill my lungs
Tears dance down my rosy cheeks like ribbons
Every breath gave me sand
It pours down my throat
Heavy and thick
Robbing me of air
The panic spreads even more
The sand coursing through my veins
It drowned me
The foggy mist lies in-between colossal pine trees
Towering plants stare at me like silent sentries
Witnessing the solar eclipse sends shivers down my spine
Leaning against the vast, contorted tree
Its sticky sap like the poisoned back of a toad, burns my hand
Pulling it away just to see the flesh escaping
Poison eating me alive
Eagerly ambling towards the sounds of unknown voices
Racking with an onslaught of sobs and tears
Thoughts of confusion explode in my head
Dumps of bloody corpses lay frozen on the ground
Skin scraped off by the asphalt

Bones crashed and crippled all over the place
A murky shadow appears
I turn to see nothing
The smell of fresh gore fills my nostrils
Provoking my nausea to rise
Until I feel two cold hands touch my neck
Chills crawl up to my cheeks
Cheeks stained with an unforgettable fountain of tears
A strange feeling of stinging creeps up my ears
Droplets of scarlet-red dripping down
The paleness on my face starts matching my shirt
Realising that it's beginning to be stained with blood
A meat-thirsty wolf comes in sight
Clenching a corpse in their serrated teeth
But before my vision begins to blur
It stares back at me
Eyes wide.
Round, gagged.
But alive.

**Martyna Rokowska (15)**
Broomfield School, Southgate

# Dear Planet Earth

Dear Planet Earth
Your greens are now faded orange, darker than ever
More strong winds blow your perfection
Your spirits are going away as the years go on
Just like time, yours is running out
Wildfires burning;
Tax and bills rising;
Temperatures climbing;
Animals and plants suffocating;
Explosions destroying;
The Earth is dying.
One year after the other
More world crises start to occur;
Damaging and breaking the wellbeing of our Mother
We are hurting our dear lover
Her love lifts this planet as we thrive
But as we evolve, she struggles to survive
We, as her children
Should love and respect our Mother
For providing us life
But we are being selfish and greedy with what Mother
provided us
Making us the virus of the Earth
With our change of hearts
And our ideas on changing for the better
Mother will be healthy and continue to be there with us

Not just her but all organisms in the world
It's not too late to change for the better
For the better of the world
For the better of the future generation.

## Melanie De Figueiredo (14)
Broomfield School, Southgate

# London

As swift as cheetah, as comfortable as a dog's life
That's what living in London is like
Grey, blunt and rough edge of a knife
Need to be vigilant, a member can strike
We are stuck in a capitalist Belvedere
Money, money and money, careful from the disconsolate sphere
Rich gets richer until his ATM dies
Poor get debts and wait until his paycheck arrives
Some need sleep, some need money
Some still think about their life-long journey
It's time to look at the mirror
Or we could get scammed by a transferrer
Stats are dreadful, devotion is incredible
We will be successful, remember nothing is impossible
We have been through our lows
Time is not far, when we will glow
Remember London's an emotion of 9 mil
Now it's our time to thrill.

## Hassan Ejaz (14)
Broomfield School, Southgate

# Black In 2022

Roses are red
I am black
My life is blue
Yet I am a human in 2022
I get looked at, scoffed at
As if I were an abandoned cat
People fear me
Yet I have done nothing to them
My parents don't let me out much
Because they are afraid
Scared I might get recruited to a gang
Or worse, end up dead
The world is cruel to people
But triple as hard when you are black
Especially a young black boy
Living in most parts of the world
The hatred I see online makes me want to cry
Sometimes I wonder in pain what did we do to deserve this?
Years of slavery and we fought for our freedom yet many
voices are not heard
Sometimes I wish was white so I could be as free as a bird
Roses are red
Violets are blue
I am black
In 2022.

**Diamond Simpson (13)**
Broomfield School, Southgate

# Vilomah

May purgatory come upon us
A wilted flower rests on the table,
The scarlet complexion -
A child,
Limp and torpid,
Her body bleeds cardinal wine on the ligneous surface
I hark back to the ample breath of being -
And yet,
Her body remains staggered
While my heavy pulse plagues,
Her ichor imprints its fingers onto the paper of my palms
The heavens are singing their choirs,
He has made his decision;
I do not dare taste the nectar engulfing my palms,
And yet,
It blankets my limbs, stomach, chest
As I oblige her shackled and lustreless wrists,
We plummet
She -
And all that she lit and grew -
Suffocated.

**Irina Mechkarova**
Broomfield School, Southgate

# The Girl

Every night, on this street
Just before twelve begins
The standing lights flicker
Quiet reaches the robins
A girl can be seen
Swaying from side to side
You can't see an expression
Just a mouth grinning wide
She begins to turn
A dagger in her clutch
And to her right there is a house
Which she finds she must touch
She wouldn't be seen again
She only had one expedition
But then you hear a scream
And pray it's the television.

## Isabel Dempsey (13)
Broomfield School, Southgate

# Karate: The Way Of Life

The feeling of comfort
The smell of sweat
The adoration for kumite
The touch of peace
The way of life
The warmth of hope
The determination to kata
The smiles all around
The way of life
When it's tough, chums feel glum
Then we remember our journey
It has only begun
Karate an art
A passion of mine
It will stay with me forever, in my heart
It is my way of life.

## Maria Syrichas (13)
Broomfield School, Southgate

# Our World

Imagine the forests without the trees,
Imagine the hive without the bees.
Imagine the goodbye without the wave,
Imagine the scared without the brave.

Imagine the day had no night,
Imagine the war with no need to fight.
Imagine the thunder with no lightning,
Imagine the scary not progressing to frightening.

Imagine the shadow without the light,
Imagine the wrong without the right.
Imagine the sun without the rain,
Imagine the wound without the pain.

Imagine the danger without the action,
Imagine the emotion without the reaction.
Imagine the mountain without the snow,
Imagine the bomb without the blow...

**Olivia Gardner (12)**
Cramlington Learning Village, Cramlington

# What Inspires You?

Everyone has an inspiration,
Whether it be someone or something.
Use your imagination,
Be creative and keep the ideas flowing.

Let the thoughts surround your mind,
Because they are part of your creative side.
They are there to help you find
What creativity lies within the inside.

Anyone can be what they want to be.
Use your inspiration to inspire you
And let your imagination run free.
Use your imagination for what you want to do
And don't let the negative thoughts try to stop you.

Thoughts can stick to you like glue,
Whether or not they are positive.
Positive thoughts are a great view.
They can also be extremely supportive.

Supportive words are amazing,
They help quite a bit.
And they're blazing,
So try. Have a go at it!

If you feel like no one wants to listen,
Then I would recommend writing.
Find your imagination,
And let your writing strike like lightning.

**Jessica Neal (12)**
Cramlington Learning Village, Cramlington

# Poison

Like a plague in your heart.
Words, like boulders, crushing those they fall upon.
The ruthless feeling that no one cares about you;
someone different in the eye of one.
Someone crushed by words.
Words that feel like poison and hit like waves.
Rumours that spread like the plague.
The echoes of whispers crashing through your head:
the words,
the rumours,
the whispers.
They deceive.
Because
now they're not just words,
now they're not just rumours,
now they're not just whispers.
Now they are problems.
Salty tears drip to the floor,
a dark cloud fogging your vision.
The mirror lies.
Your eyes lie.
That's the poison;
this poison doesn't have an antidote,
this poison always lingers,
this poison hides the truth,

because the truth is -
you're pretty
you're amazing
you're perfect.

## Eva-May Smith (13)

Cramlington Learning Village, Cramlington

# Isolation

It was all going well at first,
Until they were able to seek power.
They would dictate who I could see,
Who I could message,
How much time I could have with people.

They were thirsty for more.
There were more threats and slurs.
Then realisation hit them.
They had to stop.

It was all going well again,
But the thirst for power hit again.
This time worse,
Death threats had begun.

Memories, flooding back,
Couldn't go out again,
Couldn't message again.
It was the same, but different.

One night, I had enough.
Had a phone call.
Everything had changed,
No more control.

It wasn't over,
Stares from across the room.
Controlled, his friends instead,
Will this cycle ever end?

Friendships ruined
Due to the thirst for power.
Will it ever be over?

## Ellie Kennedy (15)
Cramlington Learning Village, Cramlington

# A Poem Written By A Turtle

My life was good.
It was amazing until you came,
Until you humans came and left it in ruins!
My home is nearly destroyed.
All because you could not follow one rule -
Recycle!
My little sister is dead because of you
So is my mother, father and brother.
They choked on plastic
Suffocated on plastic made 'not to harm us'
You created a plastic planet.
You did this.
You made this monster of a planet;
How will you make up for what you've done?
Are you sure you like this?
Down here in the ocean, it is a dump.
We have nowhere to hide,
Nowhere to live
And no oxygen to breathe.
Soon we will be extinct
Unless you do something better for us all.
Help me to rebuild my home;
Recycle.

Please.
The ocean is no longer a home,
It is a dump.
I beg you -
Help us.

## Jodie Turnbull (13)
Cramlington Learning Village, Cramlington

# Suffocating

Fire burning high and low,
Beneath the layers of ice and snow.
I feel warmth yet,
They are stone-cold.
They're falling, falling
Deeper and deeper
In sorrow and despair,
The spaces between, they seem so rare.
It's changed.
No longer is it cold.
The fires burned through ice and snow.
It's taken them beneath the stone,
And I'm in a whirlpool,
From life to death.
In misery, they slept
In the flames.
My heart kept
The one memory
Of family and friends.
That's worth the living yet
I think of those around me,
On the floor.
Through the door
Their families grieving.
I feel no more

Heat around
Sparks going down.
And I'm left standing.
Fire burning, high and low.
Beneath the souls all alone.

## Ruby Kennedy (11)
Cramlington Learning Village, Cramlington

# Love Is A...

Love is a candle
It doesn't last forever
Glows brighter and brighter
Then disappears
It's hot to the touch
Like the surface of the sun
But cold like ice

Love is a stick
It's easily broken
Once it's snapped
It can't be undone
It's rough to the touch
Like all those old memories
They are all different
Like what love is to me

Love is a storm
Of wind and rain
It's damaging, agonising
And unpredictable
It can be as strong as the winds
Of Great Storm Arwen
But the rain is the tears
Of people in heartbreak.

**Alyssa McKeown (14)**
Cramlington Learning Village, Cramlington

# The Grape

The grape that flew out my nose,
And oh, how it rolled,
It fell off the table without control,
Like how my emotions were so exposed.

The grape that flew out my nose,
And as my friend's humour goes,
The grape is not deep if it's not deep in your nose.

The shape of the grape was so beautiful,
But it was ruined when it flew out of my nose,
If only the sponge wasn't there at that time,
Maybe the grape would've made it out alive,
If only the amazing grape survived,
Then maybe no one would've cried at the sight.
The grape that flew out my nose...

**Ruby Williamson (12)**
Cramlington Learning Village, Cramlington

# Alone

Do you know what it feels like?
What it feels like to be alone?
It's like being stranded on an island.
Stranded and unknown.
Well Sarah,
oh poor Sarah, feels this way.
You'll see her standing on the beach
with a single tear running down her face.
Sometimes she'll stay there
for hours or for days;
if you see her out there,
don't just stand and stare.
For you never really know what's going on inside someone's head.

## Izzy Moretti (12)
Cramlington Learning Village, Cramlington

# Earth Is Dying

*Haiku poetry*

Beauty, around us
Burned and broken to ashes
This is now our fate.

Ripples on water
It floats up to a black void
This could end us all.

Trees tower on us
Cut, and broken to pieces
Extinction is fate.

Humans on the land
Fighting the Earth's big effort
We fight a bad fight.

It all goes downhill.
There are changes we need now -
We do need them now.

**Ethan Vaughan (13)**
Cramlington Learning Village, Cramlington

# Deforestation - A Squirrel's Tale

My home has been destroyed.
I've lost my parents,
and the big men have killed them.
They nearly killed me -
my entire family is dead.
As a squirrel, this life is horrid.
My home, friends and family have been destroyed
because of the big men taking down my home
because you couldn't follow
one
simple
rule.

**Sophie Lydon (12)**
Cramlington Learning Village, Cramlington

# Halloween!

Pointed hats and dark-winged bats,
Little black cats, sat on spooky doormats,
Scary pumpkins shining bright,
This is the night when vampires bite,
Knocking on doors trying not to get a fright,
Because it is Halloween tonight!

## Aimee Guyan (12)
Cramlington Learning Village, Cramlington

# Sinful Lands

Our Earth is full of sin
I know this first-hand.
One sin could come from a measly tin
This hourglass is running out of sand.

*BC*
Messed up times
People were slaughtered left and right.
Being alive was considered a crime
This was a time of fright.

*AD*
From AD things only got worse
Expect it to be better, you will find you are wrong.
Everyone was carried away in a hearse
Send them to hell, last thing they will hear is a gong.

*1500*
People began to get smart
But this never stopped the death that occurred.
Slaves pulled many a cart
While more and more people's visions were blurred

*1900*
A caning here and a caning there
No one could escape.
When it started the Victorian era
Not even the children got away without a scrape

*Present*
What have we done?
We have ruined each other.
I pray that this sin can be undone
Or our next generation will be lost in another.

## Isabel Groves (12)
Edgbarrow School, Crowthorne

# Planet B

We don't know if there is a planet B
Where will the last standing tree be?
Will the human race just run off and flee?
But where, oh where, is this planet B?

My mum, my dad, my sister, my son,
At this rate pollution has won,
When the sun is too hot and life is undone,
Where, oh where is this planet B?

Poverty, racism, criminals, liars,
Terrorism, extremism, big tree fires,
What will we do with animals in wires?
So where, oh where is this planet B?

Hide, run!
Duck, there's a gun!
Wars and refuge ain't no fun,
Please tell us where, oh where is this planet B?

I guess time is up,
No one took action - this ain't a bluff
The world is a mess, just our luck...
Because there isn't, oh there isn't a world named planet B.

**Isobel Dutton (11)**
Edgbarrow School, Crowthorne

# The Cry Of Earth

*Haiku poetry*

Our great treasure, Earth
The planet we kill slowly,
Help save our nature.

So much destruction,
Human pollution and waste,
Help save the forests.

## Tobi Kilvington (12)
Edgbarrow School, Crowthorne

# The Queen

We all have feelings on the royals,
some are miles apart.

We all know the Queen,
a constant from the start.

The longest-reigning monarch,
in service till the end.

Rarely seen out walking,
without a corgi friend.

As a young girl,
she grew up in a house in Marylebone.

Her uncle's abdication,
meant succession to the throne.

She will disappear from postage stamps,
her face will leave our pound.

She was only 25,
the day that she was crowned.

While the government were partying,
she sat alone and masked.

She knew responsibility,
she did what was asked.

She leaves behind 4 children,
8 grandchildren, 12 great.

A 70-year reign,
no doubt Charlie's had to wait.

So respect each other's feelings,
and what they're feeling now.

## Reece Preston (13)

Greenfield Community College, Newton Aycliffe

# The Future

We all dream of a future that is harmonious and clean,
Full of tech, science and major disease all long been.
Hover cars and trips to Mars, everything much faster,
Everyone is equal, so there's no need for a master.

Some people are part robot, there is no need to scream,
It may be far away, but it is still just a big dream.
But if we want it to be real, there's lots we must do,
Before we think of it being real we need to remember the
other things too!

Fossil fuels pollute the skies and trash pollutes the oceans,
Deforestation and discrimination can't be healed by lotion.
Poverty across the land, environments being destroyed,
Most of us doing nothing makes some of us annoyed.

So - if you want to make a change to heal the people's
screams,
You need to help the planet to get us all closer to that
dream.

**James Dean (11)**
Greenfield Community College, Newton Aycliffe

# Poem-Ception

Writing a poem
seems simple, doesn't it? Well it isn't.
It's like digging a bottomless pit
all these ideas pushing you deeper down
causing an inner conflict.

The structure of a poem can make your brain disappear
with similes, metaphors and onomatopoeia!
Singing with symbolism staring straight at you,
should it be an acrostic, ballad or haiku?

When writing a poem, you think of an ending that suits
but the actual ending can go down many routes.
Some choose to end with a cliffhanger in cases
whilst some choose to leave your mind running races.

**Owain McTighe (15)**
Greenfield Community College, Newton Aycliffe

# Christmas In The War

Christmas should be jolly
decorating with holly.
Instead we're stuck in the muck and
I'm writing this book -
bombs shook
the wooden supports,
we fought, fought, fought.

*Rip!*
The intense sound
rips the ground
that surrounds
my head.
Piercing screams
horrible dreams -
the pain.
It burns.
It surges like a fire raging on like a demon
tormenting my brain. I close my eyes...
Will we be home by Christmas?

**Isach Moore (14)**
Greenfield Community College, Newton Aycliffe

# Bullying Is Wrong

**B** ullying is something that no one wants to experience or tolerate

**U** nite against bullying and make a difference

**L** ook out for bullies and try to help those who have become victims of bullying

**L** earn how to keep yourself strong to not be affected by the bullying

**Y** ou should stand up for those who cannot defend themselves

**I** think bullying is not acceptable and should stop immediately

**N** ever bully someone because you wouldn't feel happy if you were bullied

**G** o and help other people if they were bullied by talking to them about their situation.

**I** s bullying tolerable? No, it is not and it should never happen

**S** chool is a place that can most commonly have bullying.

**W** rong things are spoken or wrong actions occur during bullying

**R** ight the wrongs that bullies have done to their victims

**O** nly you can stop the impact of bullying

**N** o one should ever experience bullying

**G** et help from an adult as soon as you can.

## Ethan Jiang (11)
Jordanhill School, Glasgow

# Ukraine, The Country Of Hope

Imagine a place, luscious and green,
a place of blue skies, a pitch-perfect scene.
Their flag ripples like the beating heart of their nation,
a station with stops leading not to starvation.
A place humming with life, a place of opportunity,
a place of unity and a kind, loving community.
A place of brilliant sunsets, a heaven-bound train,
this was a place called Ukraine.

Now imagine a place, bombs fall from the sky,
a child screams, a mother cries.
A yellow and blue flag lies lifeless on the ground
a once great nation is now found drowned.
Now imagine an endless field of debris,
a treeless land, a place drained of glee.
Smoke fills the sky, a violent man's domain,
this is a place called Ukraine.

Now answer me this, truthfully and without a grin,
which one would you rather live in?
Through the smoke, the flashes of fire
we will rise from the ashes, stand up and inspire.
Our friendship and hope will lead the way
as we ride into the sunset to a new day.

So, which will you choose, my dear loving friend?
Will it be the country nearer the end?
Will it be fields of flowers in bloom
far, far away from fears of doom?

## Ewan Pilsworth (13)
Jordanhill School, Glasgow

# Paying Bills: The Ultimate Truth

The cost of living, going up faster and faster,
The price of living, going higher and higher,
Soon we will all be with no more money,
And that means no more Christmas,
And maybe no more Halloween.
When you are slow, when you feel low,
Still, you have to pay.
Sometimes you may have to go uphill.
Sometimes it may be a downhill.
Remember, we still have to pay.
At times we cry.
At times we are dry.
Still, we have to pay.
We pass, we fail.
We can be last and pale.
Remember, we still have to pay.
People brawl, people crawl.
Still, you have to pay.
The only truth is the bill.
War or peace, gain or miss.
We still have to pay.
Maybe you're sad or you go mad.
After all of that, don't feel bad, we still have to pay.

**Ryan Roy (12)**
Jordanhill School, Glasgow

# Running Out Of Time...

Save our Earth
The place you live
The place you breathe
The place you are right now
We have not got long
We are destroyers
Killers
Taking advantage of the beautiful Earth we have
Taking advantage of the only place we have
The animals too
Live alongside us
As we destroy
Habitats of poor creatures who want nothing but peace
Yet you do not get it
The Earth is heating up
Extremes are more extreme
We need to stop now
Listen
Act now
Or soon our Earth will be wasted
Nothing left
Not you
Not me
Nothing.

## Leila Rowe (12)

Jordanhill School, Glasgow

# Acrostic Poems

**L** ong life is
**I** rreplaceable and is full of
**F** un and
**E** xciting times.

**L** asting love with
**O** ne special person on
**V** alentine's day can be
**E** xciting.

**H** appiness is
**A** plate of
**P** ancakes and a bowl full of
**P** opcorn which is really
**Y** ummy.

**S** unny days in
**M** y back garden
**I** s all I need to
**L** ighten up my thoughts
**E** very day.

**F** antastic people who
**R** eally make me happy in real life and on the
**I** nternet
**E** very day, and
**N** ever
**D** o they make me feel
**S** ad.

## Calum Anderson (12)

Jordanhill School, Glasgow

# One Infinity

We are all the same
Who said we aren't?
Race is just a name
How haven't we learnt?

There are endless numbers
In infinity
But one is the number
We must all be

One Earth, one voice
Now everybody has a choice
You can make the decision I know is right
And join the anti-racism fight

'Cause who said we have differences?
Who said we aren't the same?
'Cause whoever did mustn't have been completely sane
We are one Earth, one voice

And there are endless numbers
In infinity
But one is the number
We must all be!

**Lily Weir (11)**
Jordanhill School, Glasgow

# War In Ukraine

Putin is bad he is very sad,
Why did he start a war?
Only to cause destruction and mayhem.
He has made millions of people evacuate only to hate him,
We should support Ukraine to stop the pain.
You are 19 years old, and you help Ukraine,
You dig trenches without wrenches,
You are alone, the only thing you have is your gun.
When you shoot, even when it's night,
You hold your gun tight.
You smell like gunpowder, your hair, hands, clothes and shoes,
No matter how many times you lose,
You refuse to leave the war until you win.
You will refuse to leave until Ukraine begins to bin Russia.

**Krishna Vundavalli (11)**
Jordanhill School, Glasgow

# Schizophrenia

They scream at me, inside and out
The creepy calico clown in the crowd has started to shout
But I can't tell, for I'd be looked at as a crazy
I don't know why, I did nothing wrong
The intrusive ones are small and unseen, others are obvious
Signs start as early as teens
It almost feels like depression
It takes away all my expression
The world looks at me like I am evil
The voices tell me it's true
I still don't know what to do
I try medication
It makes me feel worse
This all feels like a looming curse.

**Charlotte Teece (12)**
Jordanhill School, Glasgow

# The Downside To The Media

Snapchat, TikTok, Instagram and more
Polluting our minds they are controlling!
I wish we could go back to how it was before
Hours spent scrolling...
Looking at people that you wish to see
Photoshopped images
I wish to be free...
Belittling messages
Telling *you* who to be.
So suddenly you have no time
It has sucked you in,
You've lost your chance
Maybe next time only a glance.
Time and time it happens again
The same old story over and over
What happens then?

**Hannah Kainth (12)**
Jordanhill School, Glasgow

# Darkness Where There Is Hope

Times were dark, times were tough
A storm of darkness rose over us
Times were dark, times were rough
A glimpse of hope came out of the fuss

April was the cruellest month
As months went by, there was no change
A glimpse of hope came out again
Words were said, freedom restored
But not for long as we explored

We all thought it was over, but not for long
But everyone still stayed strong
Numbers went up as we loosened out
But better things came about.

**Tom Sloane (12)**
Jordanhill School, Glasgow

# Rain Must Fall

Every now and then rain must fall
Whether we like it or not
The weather will never be stopped
And every now and then rain must fall.

If you're walking to school in the morning
Or returning from work in the eve
A drizzle is always a peeve
But every now and then rain must fall.

Once it comes down from the clouds
It gives life to the plants and the trees
Meaning food for the sweet bumblebees
So every now and then rain must fall.

**Andrew Black (12)**
Jordanhill School, Glasgow

# Climate Change

C old weather is gone
L iving creatures losing homes
I ncrease of wildfires
M ore storms
A ntarctic ice melting
T he polar bears dying
E ven more droughts

C ities you can't live in
H igher sea levels
A nimals going extinct
N ot enough help
G reat amount of pollution
E very life at risk.

## Millie Johnstone (12)
Jordanhill School, Glasgow

# Climate Change

We need to stop climate change
It's killing animals and sinking countries
Floods and droughts are way more common
So are storms and heatwaves
If we continue like this much longer
We may not be here to wonder
We need to stop climate change
Animals are becoming extinct
Polar bears, turtles and tigers
Do we want them gone?
No!
We need to stop climate change

## James Lowdon (12)
Jordanhill School, Glasgow

# Pollution

**P** lastic pollution in our
**O** ceans
**L** ying, waiting for its prey
**L** ittle animals getting hurt
**U** nder the sea
**T** hey are trying to escape
All the plast **I** c
Fr **O** m all the bottles, packets and plastic things
This **N** eeds to stop!

Make a change now!

**Ellie Johnstone (12)**
Jordanhill School, Glasgow

# Inevitable Is Death

With every breath it is the last I will take.
For every wrong it'll be my last mistake.
For every step my legs will break.
And for every punishing my hands shall shake.
Even though my life is gone, my memories will live on long.
But on the battlefield my ghost will roam.
Not straying far from my long-dead bones.

## Jessica Doran (13)
Jordanhill School, Glasgow

# Climate Change

We, the chosen, will fix the things they've broken
With no change, many will be dead, the world filled with
dread
Stop the change in climate change
Eating less red meat is a feat
Better for your heart and the heart of the planet
Less cattle farming, start gardening
Less CO2, less drought for you!

**Euan Palmer (12)**
Jordanhill School, Glasgow

# Bullying

**B** ullying can kill
**U** nderneath crying, outside laughing
**L** ying
**L** iving life sad and broken
**Y** ou would cry if you were in this position
**I** n bed crying
**N** ever leaving the house
**G** et advice before taking your life.

## Joel McEwan (12)

Jordanhill School, Glasgow

# Deforestation

Trees are burning
Everyone's stomach is churning
All the fire
It's only getting higher
Crash go the branches
All of those that get scratches
The homes of those
That the debris always shows.

**Ethan McLean (12)**
Jordanhill School, Glasgow

# Changing The World

How to change the world
Is a question that's been kindled
It doesn't happen in a day
And it doesn't happen at night

G7 leaders won't help
And we won't fix it by 2023
We're being too slow
And it has to happen fast

Climate change, plastic pollution
Be quick - we need a solution
Are you ready to save the world?
Because, truly, you will be whirled

Put your rubbish in the bin
Make sure it's in
Don't use a lot of water
Or the world will get hotter

Please recycle your rubbish
Oh, don't get sluggish
Save the seas
And the bees

'Cause we're all important and there is no Planet B.

## Elilta Angosom (11)
King Edward VI Handsworth Wood Girls' Academy, Birmingham

# Equality For All

We deserve our voices to be heard,
We want peace, not war
We want equality amongst all
We don't want to start a fight
We want peace, ye were right
If you want to help us the rules are simple

We want our voices to be heard
We want our views to be seen
We want peace, not war
We want equality amongst all.

People still suffer in the world,
Palestine, Yemen, Syria and Africa
Suffering from starvation
They need our help
And that's what we are to give them
They are suffering but still full of hope
Hoping someone will help
If you want to help us the rules are simple,

We want our voices to be heard
We want our views to be seen
We want peace, not war
We want equality amongst all.

The rules are simple
Oh simple they are
Little children in
Somalia, Nigeria
Crying for our help
If you want to help us the rules are simple,

We want our voices to be heard
We want our views to be seen
We want peace, not war
We want equality amongst all.

## Fatimah Bibi (11)

King Edward VI Handsworth Wood Girls' Academy, Birmingham

# Lies

Our homes are dying and these are real cases,
But people are more interested in dolling up their faces,
People follow the 'trends' just to feel important,
One day they say "Stop deforestation,"
The next day they say "Stop air contamination,"
Despite all our protests and pleading,
We need to realise actions are better than fleeing,
As every second and every day passes,
I wonder if we have time to rewrite the verses,
Earth has given more than enough to us,
But look at how we repaid it,
We need to fight for our future before it's too late,
Or else we will face a terrible fate.

## Ubaydah Adenuga (11)

King Edward VI Handsworth Wood Girls' Academy, Birmingham

# Elizabeth The Great!

Queen Elizabeth, oh where have you gone?
You were the one that always simply shone
The shimmering and shining jewels and gold
That are left so your story can be told
You spent most of your life on the throne
All over the country, you were well known
You were as twinkling as a shooting star
As the Queen of England, your reign went far
You have served this country for very long
You're the main reason why we are so strong
Oh how we all wish that you would come back
You were such a beautiful, kind lilac
I'll tell you something and this is quite true
Everyone here will never forget you.

**Imaan Ishtiaq (12)**
King Edward VI Handsworth Wood Girls' Academy, Birmingham

# It's Our Generation

To some, I may be seen as lonely
But deeper I have a soft heart
Sometimes it's steel
Although never gives up

Sometimes tired
Others energetic,
But always happy and wish it to all

Although I'm not seen as all of this,
I can still express it through this poem
I'm not seen much but have a warm heart to others

I may be the best at new things,
All I can say is have a go
This could make you happy and even make you the show!
Now you inspire yourself and be yourself and go with what
you know.

**Parmeet Kaur (12)**
King Edward VI Handsworth Wood Girls' Academy, Birmingham

# Climate Change

The world is dying in our hands,
when will we stop killing our lands?
Our future is not looking so bright
instead, it looks as dark as night.
Please stop destroying the world
as our actions will *not be ignored.*
The world will soon cease to exist
as our forces will not be dismissed.
It's absolutely shameful because
the *consequences* are going to be painful.
I hope you're all ready for the worst
because we're all going to be cursed.
Please stop hurting us all and end climate change.

## Saimah Yasmin (11)
King Edward VI Handsworth Wood Girls' Academy, Birmingham

# The Teacher

There's a priest on the roof
who descended from the skies.
He plunged down on the schoolyard
where he took us by surprise.

He looked a little startled,
but after a while
he made sure we were occupied
and cracked a wicked smile.

He melted all the monkey bars
he solved the toughest problems
with simplicity and ease,
with calculated answers.

I doubt we'll get rid of him
but I don't care or think it's fair.
I just want my old teacher back,
Mr Hamsack.

## Aliza Rafaqat (12)
King Edward VI Handsworth Wood Girls' Academy, Birmingham

# Life, What Is Life?

Life is too short,
Time passes by,
We spend time with family and friends but we all know,
Life will finish in a blink of an eye,
Don't waste it as there is only a bit of time left,
Think of what to do because
Your life is quickly being shortened every day.
One day it will be over,
One day you will see God in front of you.
Life, life is the most prized thing on Earth.
Just like how liquid evaporates, our lives will too.
The end is near,
Life, what is life?

**Aanya Kochhar (11)**
King Edward VI Handsworth Wood Girls' Academy, Birmingham

# Right At This Moment...

What are you doing *right at this moment?*
Are you with a loved one?
Are you warm and cosy?
Are you full of food?

Someone, somewhere, *right at this moment,*
Is sleeping on a bench,
Is lying lonely without a friend,
Is trying to find some scraps to fill their stomach.

Someday, some time, or *right at this moment,*
Why not serve others?
Why not donate a food parcel?
Why not give a simple smile?
*I believe you can!*

**Inayah Begum (11)**
King Edward VI Handsworth Wood Girls' Academy, Birmingham

# Don't Dream For It, Work For It

Don't always dream about things
Work for it
Nothing is ever impossible
You just have to pick the right path and the right decisions
You can be, do or achieve whatever you want to do
Never give up
Remember anything is possible
Honestly, enjoy life
You only live once
Just remember it's okay to not feel okay sometimes
Make sure you enjoy life as much as you want
Follow your dreams
No one is stopping you
Take care.

## Ronika Taghizadeh (11)
King Edward VI Handsworth Wood Girls' Academy, Birmingham

# The Haunted House

The haunted house where nobody goes,
Is it spooky? No one knows.
Ghouls and demons thirsting for crimson, scarlet blood
Or a soul to devour and eat and keep people's souls for
eternity.
The ominous sky filled me with curiosity
Thinking *is this house, this eerie house, real?*
The penetrating sound of ghouls filled my ears like a
continuous drum. Intimidated.
Haunted...

**Eliza Salam (12)**
King Edward VI Handsworth Wood Girls' Academy, Birmingham

# Happiness Never Dies

You might feel sad, but that is not bad,
You might feel angry, you are very hangry,
You are loud, you are proud,
I'm happy, and also snappy,
It is wrong to sing this song,
But I am light in the moon bright,
I love my friends, they never offend,
I like my teachers, they are like heroes,
I'm always happy and will never die.

## Safah Hussain (11)
King Edward VI Handsworth Wood Girls' Academy, Birmingham

# All About Love

Love is fake
Never will anybody say
Our love was perfect
I thought you were my ying to my yang
I thought we were in the right places
But I was wrong
I hated everything about our love
We weren't a team
Nobody will ever convince me.

*(Read it backwards now)*

**Gurleen Kaur (11)**
King Edward VI Handsworth Wood Girls' Academy, Birmingham

# This Is Me

I love to write stories
I love to try something new
I love to put things in categories
But to believe me it is up to you

I love to spend time with my family
I love to write down my thoughts
I love to spread my music
And I'd die for drawing lots.

## Ruqyyah Fatima (12)
King Edward VI Handsworth Wood Girls' Academy, Birmingham

# A Neglected Crisis

Climate change is a crisis.
So is war.
So we put sanctions and soldiers in place to help stop it.

Climate change is a crisis.
So is poverty.
So we open food banks and charities to combat it.

Climate change is a crisis.
So is crime.
So we introduce punishments and deterrents to prevent it.

Climate change is a crisis.
So are war, and poverty, and crime.
Yet we put little effort and money into climate change.

Climate change is a crisis.
But its only sanctions are speeches by its only soldiers, who are children.
Its only charities are new, with not much money and rely on activists.
Its only punishments are a few, cheap fines that the authority doesn't enforce.

If climate change is a crisis,
It must be treated in the same way as all the other crises.
Because if we are capable of tackling war, and poverty, and crime,

Then we can also tackle climate change.

## Charlie Colaco (13)
Marden High School, North Shields

# Seasons Through The Senses

Spring
The crisp white blossom, green leaves and flowers
The smell of dew and freshly-cut grass
The hopeful notes of birdsong carried on the air
The promise of warmer days to come.

Summer
The blue, cloudless sky above the dry scorched earth
The scent of meat grilling on the barbecue in the sunlight
The endless high-pitched chirping of crickets
The desire for cooler days.

Autumn
The green of trees suddenly turning into red and amber
The crisp sound of leaves crumbling beneath feet
The tempting fragrance from pinecones and roasting pumpkins
The excitement for Christmas.

Winter
The leafless trees shivering in the frost
The crunch of snow under wellies
The inviting odour of crackling fires to warm freezing hands
The desperation for the darkness to be over.

**Aaron Richardson (12)**
Marden High School, North Shields

# Earth Life

Life on the Earth is hard,
We take and take but never give back.

As we steal more and more,
We slowly kill our precious core.

As the green turns to grey,
The fires we spark burn away.

The Earth does not control what we do,
Only we can reverse the damage we do.

So as the ice caps melt away
I call on us, we, you,
To help with a job that will take more than two.

The government won't give us a chance
So I say let's change our stance,
Let's change this world for the better,
I bet we can do it together.

**Gabriel Kennedy (12)**
Marden High School, North Shields

# Fragile Earth

The tree stretched up to the night sky with twisted hands
Trying to escape the brightly burning embers in the distance
Protecting the koala bears as the eternal flame rushed over them
In a swift, rapid movement
The wildlife slowly burning as we continue to use fossil fuels
Disrupting the
Deep ocean
Silver skies
Beautiful greenery
If we continue this
We won't be able to call the Earth our home.

**Lucy Turner (13)**
Marden High School, North Shields

# Rain Cycle

The scent of the morning dew lingers
After roaming the empty realms of the sky
Once a descending madness
Now the clouds' fallen lullaby
It would have given an eternity
Only to cascade for so long
And to then return to the above as before
That now rests all alone
To live again shortly in the sad grey clouds
To call the sky its home, not forever but for now.

## Hazell Oliver (14)
Marden High School, North Shields

# Child Earth

Young, blue and green
Running though our solar system
With father sun and mother Jupiter
Each human and creature part of his body
Made to protect him
Child Earth
But we might kill him if we don't act
For he is just a child and he is ill.

## Katie McLeod (12)
Marden High School, North Shields

# Climate Change

On Planet Earth,
Us humans live.
So much power
In one little thing.

Global warming is a big disaster,
But funnily enough,
It gets people talking!

Nature is a beautiful thing,
It's a major part of our kin.

**Toby Todd (12)**
Marden High School, North Shields

# A Lost Boy

A warm heart that once belonged to an innocent boy,
A bright intelligent kid that had a promising future,
Walked away obliviously,
Taken by the evil world's charming yet cruel supremacy,
If only he knew what direction he was being led to,

Youths like him got lured into the mentality that 'ps' were
the only thing that mattered,
Life turned for the worst from the day he started being
deceitful,
If selling sweets and drinks wasn't the option,
Surely dealing drugs was,

This wasn't the warm-hearted boy that Mum and Dad
raised,
This was the boy that got taken over by this generation,
The questioning thoughts,
The self-blaming factors that came to Mum and Dad,

They taught him the dos and donts,
The rights and the wrongs,
Everything they didn't want him to be,
He became,

The bad school reports came,
The phone calls came,
Not long till the feds also came,

Hard-working dad was stressed because of his mess,
Mum left work because of his stress,
The family fell apart because of his mess,
Nothing was the same,

Dark clouds covered the house like a blanket,
Restless nights showered onto them,
Yard became like a hotel for him,
Bringing any smell of toxic stench in,

Till this day nothing was the same,
Nothing had changed,
Now time to forget the past,
Focus on the future.

**Aizah Undre (14)**
Pearson Online Academy, London

# A Slow, Painful Death

Help me,
Help me I cry, again and again
Death is coming
Soon, very soon,
All because of the selfish humans
I do so much for them
I feed them
I give them life
I give them sunlight
I give them water
I am their mother

Mother Nature they call me,
Mother Earth
Is this how they treat their biological mothers?
Just because I am a planet, they treat me like trash and
don't take care of me?
I am the one who gives them life
Without me, they would be nothing.

Selfish humans
Selfish, selfish humans who only care about themselves
They chant, "Save the Earth"
But do they do anything?
Words without actions are just that
Empty words
Empty promises

I give them life,
And they betray me.
I am their mother,
And this is how they repay me.

Soon I will die
Little do they know
Without me
They are nothing
Absolutely nothing.
If I die
They die
"Save Mother Earth"
Humans do nothing but lie
A slow painful death we will all suffer because of their
selfishness.
A slow painful death
I can hear their cries
The regret in their voice
But alas
They brought this on themselves.

## Aasiyah Khimji (17)
Pearson Online Academy, London

# Poetical Dancer

In your eyes, I am nothing but a dancer,
In the night, I am nothing but prose,
Speak through me your words,
Speak through me your mind,
In your hand, you hold a pen,
Through your lips, you hold a story,
Move with me, this rhythm and that rhyme,
Sing to me, be emotive and thrive,

I told him once that I'd like to dance,
He just looked at me and laughed,
I frowned and took my pen and trailed back to that very
desk,
In the night, my quill dances, what pathetic fallacy shall we
add,
He's a dancer, with each drop of ink, he prances,
He has not moved a foot from his desk,

In his eyes, you are his only dancer,
In the day, you are his only friend,
Speak to me your troubles,
Lean on me when you cry,
Through your lips, you hold a story,
Within every poetical device.

**Alyssa Springer-Cupid (16)**
Pearson Online Academy, London

# Change Is Near

The time is now.
Let's make the vow.
To save the frontier,
Change is near.

Animals are dying,
Sea levels rising,
Never to be seen,
Let's make a scene.

It's time to stop.
Every last crop.
Save the water,
For our future daughters.

Storm after storm,
Is now the new norm.
Let's make Earth great,
Before it's too late.

The time is now.
Let's make the vow.
To save the frontier.
Change is near.

**Emily Oldman (14)**
Pearson Online Academy, London

# Our Planet, Our Home

I'm only young but if I can see,
The damage we're doing to our poor seas.
We're doing our best to keep it alive,
Because without the ocean nothing will thrive.
Our Earth is important, why don't you understand?
It isn't just made up of oceans and land,
There are animals galore,
But not just off the shore.
In forests, in jungles. in deserts all over,
In London, in Devon, in Cornwall, in Dover.
From birds to crocodiles, from dodos to dinosaurs,
These are all animals that worked on our shores.
Their fossilised remains show off their pains.
The dodos in particular were hunted by man,
These crucial beings were once alive,
But now down to us, they no longer survive.
Komodo dragons, macaws, and of course, the blue whales,
They are all in the markets, acting as sales.
They are all endangered, haven't you heard?
I'm sorry to say, there aren't many left,
Their hide is being stolen as part of a big theft.
Macaws are birds, they're meant to be free,
But sadly deforestation is tearing down trees.
Their numbers are decreasing, unfortunately I have to say,
But I hope that those who have already passed are in peace
as they lay

Our Earth is our home,
Our Earth is our planet,
Please don't let it go to waste,
Let's fight global warming and find a way to ban it.

**Myya Johns (11)**
Poltair School, St Austell

# The World Is An Oyster

A humid air lingers,
Residue of the storm, evaporating now.
Distant memories of the shocking spark,
Flagrant to the overflowing, everlasting peace

Irate from above and the heavens open,
Splashing and crashing on the absorbent ground,
Most conjoining to form one body.
However some fall with a throbbing echo

Speedily shooting down the drop,
Towards an alliance of similarity.
Still lost and unnerved, to an overwhelming extent.
Leaping off the edge, only cushioned by the engulfing
bubble

A sense of massiveness with little meaning,
A world within a world, seemingly wearisome and mundane.
The constant view of a further horizon. Something more,
something better

You see as the saying goes,
The world is an oyster,
And for one reason or another
I truly am the pearl.

## Ella Brooks-Richardson (16)
Poltair School, St Austell

# The King Of The Savannah

The king of the savannah lies in his bed made of gold,
peering over the beautiful savannah
whilst the impala lie in the dark below,
trembling in fear of the predator up high.

The lion feasts on the impala as the
heavy crown sits on his head, his
head is up high whilst the impala's
head lies down low, afraid to speak.
The impala graze of the thin empty grass
as the lion demolishes the meat of the herd.

Whilst the king has fun out in the wild,
the sun shining on his face,
the impala is stuck in hiding, quivering in the cold.
The impala tries to talk but is shoved back to the ground
with a face full of dirt.
The lion sits on the throne
licking his fingers full from his meal,
as the impala cries for help!

## Kara Crawford-McLeod (12)
Reddam House Berkshire, Wokingham

# My Dying World And I

All alone in my room,
Thinking of the road we are taking to doom,
People are screaming yet they are forced to abide,
As the leaders hurtle towards our mother's suicide,
Yet we still take this growing danger in our everyday stride.

All alone in my room,
Watching the flowers maybe in their last bloom,
The petals break apart to greet the bright blue sky,
They don't know they will soon die,
That the ground they grow on is growing dry.

So, I stay, alone in my room,
Watching my superior lay my tomb,
Knowing in my heart that it won't be long,
But everyone else sees nothing truly wrong,
For our mother, I must stay strong.

All alone in my room,
Watching a tower of factory fumes,
This problem is being barred,
So, I constantly must put up my guard,
But I am getting weak, and it is draining and hard.

All alone in my room,
Watching the next dreadful day loom,
Seeing animals perish on TV,

They have no Planet B,
But at least they are free of this responsibility.

Now I lie awake in my bed,
With all these crushing thoughts in my head,
But I see a light,
It is small but it is bright,
Because the hope I see is how we can make it right.

Awake in my bed,
Knowing the world is slowly turning red,
Though there must be a way,
Despairing I still stay,
And alone I continue to lay.

So, I lie awake in my bed,
Imagining life wherever I tread,
Trees that shimmer with morning dew,
Though in places forests are getting few,
We still mourn the woods we loved and knew.

Awake in my bed,
Determined the fight must be led,
But who am I,
To put forward that shallow lie,
That *soon* together we may get by.

Soon I fall asleep,
And over my world I weep,
I dream of better days to come,
A future where the war is won,

For this is my future, not theirs but mine.
They are the ones who made this mess, now it is our time.

## Dare Cross (12)
Reddam House Berkshire, Wokingham

# Why The Slaves Worked On

Slaves worked tirelessly,
Working and working for no pay
And they couldn't even imply
That they wanted to watch anime

They worked and worked and worked,
While their owners lived in plenty
The slaves wouldn't have a choice
If they wanted to be free or not

They had to listen for outside news
To see when they could be free
But the one thing they all knew
Is that they only 'hired' Africans

Lots of them rebelled,
Only to be killed
The others could only sit and watch
While their friends got penalised

Slaves worked tirelessly
Working and working for no pay
And they couldn't even imply
That they wanted to watch anime.

## Danny Royle (12)
Reddam House Berkshire, Wokingham

# I Wish I Could Open My Mouth And Sing

What have I done to you?
Why do you hate me?
Why can't you see me as what I am: human?
Is there so much difference between you and I?

I wish I could say this.

I peer through the bars of my cage
Dreaming of being you,
Hoping for light.

I flinch at the shouts screaming in my ears,
Flooding my senses.
I shed a tear as shards of glass hit my body,
Puncturing my skin.

I let the crippling fear sink in.
I bind myself to the cage in which I'm imprisoned,
Clawing at my skin
Praying to be someone else,
Hoping to shut my eyes and for them never to open.

I wish I could do something,
Anything.
But I can't.
This torment is relentless,

It's a monster waiting to attack,
It's a monstrous fire gnawing at my skin.
It's hell.

I'm scared.
I can't say everything I always wish I could say.
I hate myself for it.

So I wish I could open my mouth and sing,
I wish for freedom,
I dream of spreading my wings
And not being shot down

I wish for equality
And to be liked
By everyone
Like you.

I wish for the freedom
To do whatever I like.

I wish I could enjoy places.
I wish I wasn't frowned upon,
Or judged,
Or hurt,
Or scared,
Or hated,
Or accused,
Or look like this.
Because wherever I go, it follows me.

Everywhere I go, the monster attacks me.
No matter what, I've always done something wrong.

It isn't fair how you see me.
I am the same as you.
Why can't you see it?

I wish I could be perceived as normal.

I wish I could open my mouth and say this.

**Poppy McManus-Smith (12)**
Reddam House Berkshire, Wokingham

# Black History Month

"I float like a butterfly and sting like a bee"
I am Muhammad Ali
I am the best
I am the greatest
No one can beat me
Because I am Muhammad Ali

"Don't count the days, make the days count"
Champions are made from a vision
Like me, I am a champ because I am Muhammad Ali

I want to help the people in need
I wanted to help the community
I wanted to help people to believe they mattered
To believe they can do more than just get bullied because of
their race
Because I am Muhammad Ali

"I float like a butterfly, sting like a bee"
I am Muhammad Ali
I am the best, I am the greatest, no one can beat me
Because I am Muhammad Ali.

## Sami Syed (11)
Reddam House Berkshire, Wokingham

# This World Needs A Change

There is only one Earth
So why are we tearing it apart?
Ever since your birth
You have wrecked its heart

It is meant to be a safe place
That everywhere you look is magical
But I have some things we need to erase
So, we can make it fantastical

So why do we go to war?
Is it to take others down?
I say this cannot happen anymore
Or the whole world will close down

Battlefields are wrecked
People's families are heartbroken
These are the after-effects
People are outspoken

God didn't create this world to have fights
It was so we could be alive
We all need to take care of this delight
We have a chance to survive

Everyone should all work as a group
We need to give back
Now you will be caught in a friendship loop
So, don't attack

We should respect everyone
Admire other talents
A new revolution has just begun
Now no one is a peasant

Just so I am being clear
Wars need to end
Because we all live here
We can all be such good friends.

## Zara Bates (12)
Reddam House Berkshire, Wokingham

# Black History Month

Everyone knows him for his fame and admiration,
many think it's overrated,
he was just a simple president.
Do you really think he was a simple president?

He presided over the transition from minority law and
apartheid,
earning international respect for his race.
They beat him several times.
He got up and went back to fight.

Nelson Mandela, the symbol of equality; the patriarch of
liberty.
Do you really think these adjectives are false?
He also cheered for the Springboks,
guess what they won.

"The greatest glory is not never falling, but always getting
up"
now you think about it and surprisingly he's right again.
He's not a simple president, he is one of the best presidents.
In this special month, he should
be admired and remembered.

A phrase of him has become a part of me
"We must use time wisely and realise that it is always the
right time to do things right."

For me, this phrase is more than just words
it's a kind of life.

**Carla Cuadrado Barrero (11)**
Reddam House Berkshire, Wokingham

# Freedom

When the sun rises
I wish to be somewhere else
The silent orders from my master
Remains hanging in the air
The rays of the sun
Are merely the rays of the Arctic.

Into reality, I wake.
Pain inflicted with each step
Taken away from my freedom
Separation with a scornful barricade
I dream of the dark blue sky
Whilst others wish for a cold grey day.

So why not let me breathe the fresh air?
Why not let me sit under the dazzling sun?
Why would you give up your freedom,
When I can only dream of it?

I will demand freedom,
For that is the one thing I lack.
Like chains wrapped around my legs,
Slowly dragging me into the ground.
The cold, murky darkness,
Engulfs me.

The sun bears down on me,
Oh, how I wish I could swim,
In the cool clear waters
Of a stream.
Sitting in my room,
I stare at the walls.

With sunlight advancing,
Through the gaps of my blind.
A warm, reassuring feeling,
I will not give up my dream.

## Jerry Xie (12)
Reddam House Berkshire, Wokingham

# You Hear Their Voices

No matter your age, your gender, or race
Read this poem at a steady pace
You hear their names, Rosa and Mary
Don't pretend you find them scary

The things they lost, the things they gave
It was all to keep you safe
The brainwashed people of today
Need to listen up, and hear me say
Black History is not just a month
It's the voices of people, and not how they punch

Something as simple as sitting on a bus
Can apparently result in a heavy loss
"I have a dream" is what he said
But now Stephen Lawrence lies down dead

Don't pretend it's not your problem
Racism will be kicked to the bottom
Then Marcus Rashford will get his way
And all black people will have a say

Together we stand, we stand up tall
It's just a colour, after all
Equality shall come, it shall come soon
Then no black people will face the doom

Of being punished, because of their skin
It will no longer be a sin.

**Gwyneth Thornton (11)**
Reddam House Berkshire, Wokingham

# I Am The Slave

All day I work, tiring and long
An unseen master hiding in wealth
For I am the slave
And I have been chained

You, the innocent, you the ignorant
Hear our plea for justice
This, this terror that is our lives
Our torture is endless

Every day, the same
Work, sleep, work, sleep
For I am the slave
And I have been chained

The fire inside us, the fire of freedom
Quenched by the iciness of your heart
Crack. The whip of frost
Raking the skin off our burning backs

Despair. Misery. Hopelessness.
The grey cloud above our heads
Always raining, cold and wet
Sunshine is a thing of the past

They use their weapons of ice
They freeze us nearly dead
For I am the slave
And I have been chained

But we shall burn
Burn brighter through the frost
The fire inside us
Shall melt their chains of ice

For I am the slave
And I shall never be chained.

## Elliot Stirling (12)
Reddam House Berkshire, Wokingham

# Black History Month Poem

A little child was alone and sad,
He wanted to make friends with those people.
But Mommy said no.
Mommy said that they were bad people,
But his curiosity kept growing and growing.
He did not understand, he just wanted to see.

He came out the house and saw nothing.
Just broken houses and rundown cars.
Our neighbours were gone,
Mommy said they went to a magical place.
Where equality lies, and peace lives.

There's an invisible wall, between him and them.
Large signs written in bold, where Mommy said he should not cross.
She told him that when someone goes there,
People never come back.

But one day, he finally decided to walk past it.
He walked and walked and walked.
Crispy loud noises and he fell on the ground.
Opened his eyes, he saw clear skies.
Wind peacefully patting on his face.

Thought this might be the place Mommy talked about,
Just like she described.

## Cedric Ma (12)
Reddam House Berkshire, Wokingham

# I Am A Bird

I'm under control all the time
I was taught since childhood
Follow orders and be rewarded

I yearn for the boundless sea
But see only endless blood

I look forward to the free forest
But only saw the railing of the cage

I started to stop thinking
I started following orders

In exchange for dignity
It's the same life

I started to resist
I'm starting to get back on my feet

The insults turned into bullets
The yelling turned into law

But what am I afraid of?
Let the bullet go through my body
Let me feel every pain
Then it will become my power to run faster

The dark eyes will eventually ignite with light
The desperate eyes will be filled with hope

Abuse turns into cheers of victory
Bullets turn into salutes of victory

I am a bird
I am now a free bird.

## Darcilia Zhong (12)
Reddam House Berkshire, Wokingham

# Marcus Rashford

I wanted to help the people in times of need
I wanted everyone to be happy
I wanted to help the community
We were going to beat Covid

I suddenly thought of a plan
For those people in need
So, I gave them some food
And it spread joy to the UK

I met the Queen
I even got an OBE
I got respected by the world
But then it happened

It was the Euro final, and it went down to penalties
I stepped up to put the ball on the spot
I took the penalty and hit the post
That's the moment social media blew up

And it wasn't good
Me and my other black teammates were being racially
Abused just because we all missed penalties
Even our fans were mad

All these messages were ridiculous
All of them made me sick
But all I could do was endure the pain
Waiting for it to stop.

## Vismay Ganesh (12)
Reddam House Berkshire, Wokingham

# Bukayo Saka

When I stepped up to take it
All the pressure on my shoulders,
If I scored I would be a hero
If I missed people would treat me like a zero

It turns out it was the zero
There is no excuse for
Racist abuse towards a nineteen-year-old
Who once felt like gold

The nice letters I received
From the ones that believed
Cheered me up,
Instead of making me feel like I'd been beaten up

A couple of days after,
I went back on social media,
And apologised for missing the penalty,
But said I am not sorry for who I am
Or where I come from

I am Bukayo Saka, professional footballer
For England and Arsenal FC
Young, black and proud.

**Seth Sandhu (12)**
Reddam House Berkshire, Wokingham

# A Man Of Freedom

A son of South Africa born in 1918
Raised in the difficult times of apartheid
He led a trustworthy and rebellious team
As a lawyer, he was never tongue-tied

The colour of his skin was black
The laws of his country were not in his favour
That forced him and his army to attack
And earned him 27 years of prison food flavour

He came out of prison victorious
Becoming the first black president of South Africa
The stand for freedom and justice was glorious
His name was Nelson Mandela

On this Black History Month of October
We remember all that he has done
For rights that can be enjoyed by every voter
Thank you, Madiba, from everyone.

## Ariella Avidi (11)
Reddam House Berkshire, Wokingham

# The Black Cat

Oh, black cat, why do people think you're bad luck?
You're just the same as the others inside and out
As any other cat or dog
Why do people not go near you?
Oh, black cat, why do people only like you in October?
Is that your special month?
People only seem to want to see you then
That needs to change, all cats are the same
So why do people dodge and run when they see you?
You're all the same, even white cats or tabby cats
They're all the same, so why are you different?
All the cats are flesh and blood
Oh, black cat, I feel so bad
You know, black cat, I love you
And all the other black cats around the world too.

## Ava Dowding (12)
Reddam House Berkshire, Wokingham

# Judgement

Have you ever walked into a room and felt all eyes on you?
They give you a look up and down and talk about you,
Have you ever been isolated from the rest of the world
because of your skin?
It never makes sense why people make me feel so
chagrined,
They just grinned and acted as if they didn't apply that my
thighs being a different colour affected them,
They act as if they didn't apply a look that makes me want
to cry because of the colour of my skin,
And they act like they didn't apply a look that makes me
want to die because of the colour of my skin.

## Sophie Noone (12)
Reddam House Berkshire, Wokingham

# The Future

Let there be a new life
Let there be peace in the air
Let there be sunlight to bring happiness
Let there not be racism
Let there not be people who think they are different
Let there be diversity
Let's make a change
Our world should be better not worse
I am shocked with how the world is
Why are we doing this?
Let there be kind and generous people

Let's make a change to our world
Let's travel with our hearts
Let's bring our world to shine brighter and live better
And have a good future.

**Florence Slater (12)**
Reddam House Berkshire, Wokingham

# A World Which Is Better

Racism is dying,
It's fading away.
The world is improving,
But that's just in my head.

I imagine the future,
A world which has equality.
The leaves are dancing,
The birds are soaring through the sky.

But I'm falling from the sky,
The leaves are crawling.
The world has not changed,
And people are still dying.

We need to make a change,
Where the world is right.
Not where the population is decreasing,
Just because of someone's race.

## Chloe Dell (12)
Reddam House Berkshire, Wokingham

# My Black History Month Poem

They would get scared
They would get out of their seat
And either walk out or walk to the back

But only one stood up for themselves
One day on the
1st December 1955

She refused her seat
To a white person
Who was surprised

That such a person
Would say no
But this time she stood up for herself

She stayed till the police came
And stayed for a few hours
Then she was released

Then it started
The protesting
The freedom.

**Erin Sandhu (11)**
Reddam House Berkshire, Wokingham

# I Have Hair

I have hair,

And not just on my head.
I have hair,
All down my arms and legs.

I have hair,
It itches and it spikes.
I have hair,
But I'd never dare to shave nor wax like the other girls.

I have hair,
And it shows.
I have hair,
I don't mind but you might.

I have hair,
I hadn't thought 'bout it much before
I have hair,
It doesn't make a difference to me,
But apparently, it does to you.

## Romilly Haworth (13)
Reddam House Berkshire, Wokingham

# A Vision For The Future

A vision for the future
Where people come together
A vision for the future
Where there is peace forever

A vision for the future
Where everyone has freedom
A vision for the future
Where everyone has a choice

A vision for the future
Where people are not judged
A vision for the future
Where people are hugged

A vision for the future
Where people come together
A vision for the future
Where there is peace forever.

**Timi Owolabi (12)**
Reddam House Berkshire, Wokingham

# Even When...

Even when I was questioned by myself,
I was not prepared.
Even when I was dying,
I was not prepared.
But you were.
You were there,
Watching me die,
Didn't even hesitate to help.
Even then the people who saw it,
Were the ones who do the same,
Like you do, to me.
Even when they ask you,
You lie.
Even when they choose a nice way to ask,
You didn't say it was your fault.
Now, they have had enough of your lies.

## Millie Khin (13)
Reddam House Berkshire, Wokingham

# Caged With Rage

Every day,
I wake up seeing the sun shine brightly
Knowing I can't go out
Seeing everybody walking about
It makes me wonder ever so slightly
Why can't I see the world?
I feel so caged,
It makes me enraged.
Every night,
I'm full of fright
For the events of the next day
Full of dismay
The thing that makes me enraged
Is that I am treated as a slave
Why am I caged?
I must be brave.

**Sully Palmer (12)**
Reddam House Berkshire, Wokingham

# Familiar Face

All lives matter
it's not a race
even though everyone isn't a familiar face
there is no reason to dislike a race
so if there is a dislike, that's a disgrace

So now it's time to fight
not with fists but with our words
'cause our generation is the one that can reshape this world
so now it's time to stand for what's right
so that no more kids have to live in fright.

### Daniel Slade (12)
Reddam House Berkshire, Wokingham

# What Is Right?

Sometimes in life you need
to love yourself.
Sometimes in life you need
to care for yourself.
No matter what, you are beautiful so
be yourself.
Just because you may have a different
skin tone doesn't mean you are
not as special as everyone else.
So ask yourself
what is right?
Well, my right is to love and to cherish
myself and everyone around me.
What is your right?

**India Nicholls (11)**
Reddam House Berkshire, Wokingham

# Equality

We are all equal
We need to fight for equality
People should not be judged by the colour of their skin
But by their personality

There are still some places in the world
That judge people on their skin,
This need to stop
There needs to be a change in the world

We need to be the change that the world wants to see
We need to make sure that the world is equal
We are all equal.

**Henry Hallett (13)**
Reddam House Berkshire, Wokingham

# Black History Month

All black lives matter,
We need to spread awareness.
Racial inequality and discrimination against race
Is always in the wrong.

Everyone should be treated equally,
No matter skin, gender, or race.
Prejudice would not be acceptable
And it should be stopped.

If people are being treated by skin,
How will this be fair?
Hostility to black people
Won't be agreeable.

**Joyce Lo (11)**
Reddam House Berkshire, Wokingham

# Steps To Equality

In the dead of night,
When the birds take flight,
They crept through the stream,
Up the valley and around the woods,
Although it may seem
By their hoods
Their silent steps,
Their chains tightening with every stagger,
Their hearts throbbing from the fear of the deadly dagger,
That they have come far,
But we still have a long way to go,
Until every person is equal.

**Francesca McLoughlin (13)**
Reddam House Berkshire, Wokingham

# Racism

No matter black or white people,
We are all equal.
Every right for white,
Black people should have too.
No matter rich or poor,
They can all be white or black.
All significant people should be remembered,
If they are black or white.
We have to eliminate racism,
Everyone should do it too.
A world without racism,
Will be a better world to live in.

## Friedman Lo
Reddam House Berkshire, Wokingham

# Black Lives Matter

Innocent people are dying
Children are crying
How can racism exist?
Why do people persist?
The world should be different
We need to protect the innocent

We are all people of colours
All sisters and brothers
Be true to one and all
This should be our call

Stop
Calm down
Wipe off that frown
And don't clown around.

## Phoebe Ayton-Judd (11)
Reddam House Berkshire, Wokingham

# Black Lives Matter

Some people are free
While others flee
Screams tear at their throats
While others gloat
A life in fear
While others watch, standing near
A life of freedom, making their own choices
While others scream, covering their ears to block the noises
Always overlooked, never seen for who we are.

**Artemis Kompocholi (11)**
Reddam House Berkshire, Wokingham

# Black History Month Poem

Kind-hearted people are being killed
People are losing family
How long will it take
And how many deaths will it take
For people to change?

I hope in the future
That change will happen
The world will be equal
And no one will be discriminated against.

## Sienna Pugh (11)

Reddam House Berkshire, Wokingham

# We Are All The Same

Some make them feel shame
But at the end of the day
We are all the same

Some make them feel pain
But at the end of the day
We are all the same

Some ashamed
But at the end of the day
We are all the same.

**Emilio Aspin (11)**
Reddam House Berkshire, Wokingham

# A Risk Worth Taking

I can feel you in a star; just that one,
You scintillate against the darkness of the world,
Unnoticed like a speck but as fierce as the sun.

The truth in a lie,
You don't see it?
Neither did I.
The hope in my demons,
A perfect answer to every selfish doubt.
Could this pain deepen?

You hold the weight of a strength far too heavy to bear,
All for what?
Love they say you shouldn't share.

Every reason I have to leave you,
Is every reason I have to keep you,
Because no one can glow like you do.

Exposing the wrong in the right,
And the right in the wrong.
A risk worth taking.
Blind faith is all we have.
The world will die before they see it breaking.

Because even though you're far away, my soul,
I can feel you in that star; just that one.
And it's everywhere: a priceless glow.

## Yaynah Welsh (17)
Solihull Sixth Form College, Solihull

# 653449

Trapped in their world
Watching my world evolve outside
My own, taken every day
Fighting for breadcrumbs
Fighting for freedom
Every minute of every hour.

Trapped in their world
Electric fences shroud us
Stones eat away at my skin
Feeling myself slowly decaying
Every minute of every hour.

Trapped in their world
Living in an emotional blender
Every minute of every hour.

Trapped in their world
My nimble fingers start to shrivel
My ribcage on display: like a museum
Every minute of every hour.

Trapped in their world
Their voices bellowing in my ear
Marking me, everywhere
Every minute of every hour.

Trapped in their world
Another group taken
Where do they go?
The smell of them engulfs our lungs
Ashes cascading around us
Nobody knows about us
We are animals: here to entertain them
On display: like a museum
*Every minute of every hour.*

## Amber Ewins (16)
Solihull Sixth Form College, Solihull

# Devil's Dance

Chaos ensued at cataclysmic rates
Violence so bloody
It only filled the gods with unyielding hate.

Those same gods left us to fall and perish
In this barren wasteland where nightmares come to life
And dreams come to vanish.

Death was our only companion in this life
No warrior, no amount of strength could prepare
For the geysers of blood coated in a single knife.

Death and destruction were all I knew
War between families
Conquest was what they pursued.

Dragging their lives and humanity with them
Soldiers, children, women falling like flies
War that not even the mightiest god can condemn.

Signs of life disappear at every chance
This bloody demonic war
Was truly the devil's dance.

## Nel Kabenga (16)
Solihull Sixth Form College, Solihull

# Dead Poet

I open my eyes to the snow,
A white blanket shrouding the field,
"It's beautiful," I say,
And then I crumble.

You see,
He loved the snow,
He watched it dance
With wonder in his eyes.

I'm reminded of him now,
As the soft white specks
Land on my head, on my coat,
At my feet.

I'm reminded of him,
His Shakespearean soul,
His love of all things,
And I smile at the sky.

I scream his name,
Hoping he's somewhere in the frost,
Hoping he can hear me,
As I crumble.

**Emily Lander (16)**
Solihull Sixth Form College, Solihull

# Library Visit

*Haiku poetry*

A world's library
Walls filled with big adventures
To escape this place.

Hopeful romantics
Without another person
By their lonely side.

World-ending robots
With horrible diseases
Death to fake people.

Car chases and guns
Are enough to fuel flaming
Fires. Death to a

Hero, to the few.
Representation matters
Now more than ever.

Bookshelf with classics
The Great Gatsby, In Cold Blood
Oh, look! Young Adult.

Horrors packed on the page
Write in shining armour
Twenty-four hours in a day
Not enough time.

**Leah Berry (16)**
Solihull Sixth Form College, Solihull

# Renga

A soft whistle blows past me
Caressing my skin,
Time shifts of its own accord.

The brief change in colour,
Window to emotions,
Replica of a human soul.

Arms united to protect me,
A body to lean on for comfort and shelter,
Your heart beats *silently*.

Each visit, you embrace me,
I take it,
I give my heart to you.

You lived for many decades,
Treated with hate,
Buried. Broken. Burned.
Yet here you stand for me,
You were destroyed, close to extinction,
We fix each other, *together*.

**Isabela Sopawiro (16)**
Solihull Sixth Form College, Solihull

# Evening Storm

At eve last night the old sky wept
Great heavy tears of pain
The warming, waking sun was scared
And hid behind the rain.

At eve last night huge waves came crashing
Spitting and smashing the sand
The bountiful, beautiful fish swam fast
But drowned upon the land.

At eve last night tall trees were shaken
Their roots ripped from their place
As morning came the trees fell silent
She'd left without a trace.

**Kleio Wardle (16)**
Solihull Sixth Form College, Solihull

# You Are My Sun

You never say you miss me.
You never say you care.
You never even notice me.
Yet I'm your matching pair.

You never walk with me.
You never walk alone.
You never stop to see me.
Yet I am the opposite clone.

I am the shadow to your sun.
I'm lost within your light.
Left sacrificing things I love.
Whilst you are shining bright.

I am the darkness
Behind you.

**Marcie Allen (17)**
Solihull Sixth Form College, Solihull

# Autumn Rhapsody

Crimson and blonde,
Hues flourishing like zephyrs,
Bless autumn's flora.

Grey and frigid,
Wintry wisps hail on the realm,
A dead realm of fall.

Marigold beams,
The sun's inferno dispersed,
Casting aside rays.

Slumbered and tranquil,
Critters hibernate gently,
Preparing for spring.

Mellow and toasty,
Hot choco bubbles ooze,
Autumn has begun.

### Safa Abdi (16)
Solihull Sixth Form College, Solihull

# Back 'N' Forth With You

How is it I'm running but yet still
Stuck. But yet riding a motionless carousel,
Like a song on loop,
Back 'n' forth, but back and forth with you.
Constant lies, daily cries, obsessive thoughts,
Over and over again,
Thrilling but sad, exciting but draining,
A constant headache, a daily stress, a paranoid gut,
Over and over again,
Back 'n' forth, but back and forth with you.

**Sheree Wyatt (16)**
Solihull Sixth Form College, Solihull

# So Close, So Far

Lying under the stars,
I feel your soul breathe,
Connected, our hearts
Into the same beat.

Home.

Tears cascade on a journey
At the thought of you,
Breath sucked from my lungs,
Nightmare come true.

Alone.

Maybe we'll meet again,
Together at last,
To the end
And after... that.

## Hannah Moloney (17)
Solihull Sixth Form College, Solihull

# The Ballad Of The Sky

Brighter than the stars you are
You light up the skies
In the dark and the damp
That is where she lies.

The moon as bright as silver
You as bright as gold
Stars around you dancing
Looking from the cold.

The day is over
Song is done
Darkness creeps in
Shadow your sun.

## Fiona Higgins
Solihull Sixth Form College, Solihull

# Blasphemous

Weep tears of red into the sand
Weep tears from fear of us
Once sat upon your temple throne
Once we were blasphemous.

## Robbie English (16)
Solihull Sixth Form College, Solihull

# Falling

I freefall through his heart
And into the sunless abyss
I hit the bottom.
I sink.

## Macey Ward (16)
Solihull Sixth Form College, Solihull

# Water Sports Is Fun!

Water sports is fun
When you're getting wet
Either speeding along a wave
Or flying as high as your kite.

Do it anywhere, whether
It's windy or not, lots
To do like windsurfing
Kitesurfing, surfing and lots more.

Best not go in the water
When it's cold better go in
Water when it's warmer
Make sure you get a
Wetsuit and life jacket.

What do you think, do you want a try?

## Eddie Maclean (12)
Tiree High School, Isle Of Tiree

# True Self

Finding your true self
Is something that can
Be quite confusing
For people
Sometimes.

For some people they know
No such thing.
As their true self.
All they know is how to be
A sheep.
A sheep who follows
And copy's someone
Else.

They don't know how to
Express themselves.
So they do everything
The same as someone
Else.
All they know is how to
Be someone
They're not.

I know how it felt.
To be a sheep.
I got caught up in
Something.
Something that
I hated.
But didn't back
Out.
Because I thought people
Would think different of
Me.

It was only a while ago
That I figured out
How to become me.

I left behind everything that
Made me uncomfortable.
I started to do things I love.
I started doing things for myself.

I took my time outside of drama and
Everything else.
Took time for myself.
Did things I loved.
Wrote down all the good things.
About myself.
And other people.
To get out of the whole being someone

Else mindset.
And wrote down all *my* thoughts.

I am me.
And you are you.
There is nothing you can do
About it.
So if someone says
You're not good enough.
Forget them.
You don't need
That type of people in
Your life.

Because at the end of the day you are all you have.

## Casey Colthart (13)
Tiree High School, Isle Of Tiree

# Polar Bears, Goodbye

Now that climate change is really happening
Animals like polar bears
Are going to starve and die.

All because of us and our choices.

The ice is melting, thining
The polar bears are being forced
Off of their homes.

They have to swim up to ninety-six miles, no rest
All for them and their children to sleep.

The land is not right for them
They grow so big
And need so much
But it's hard when their food sources are close to zero.

Thirty percent of polar bears will go extinct by *only* 2050
I mean how are you supposed to live when you live on ice
for centuries and now are finding food in woodlands
Fighting grizzly bears for some lunch and dinner.

So have a heart and care!
The least you can do for these poor animals is recycle.

## Anya Wright (12)
Tiree High School, Isle Of Tiree

# War

In Ukraine, every day people die no matter who they are.
War crimes are being committed everywhere.
No matter what the country they will have committed a war crime.
But it's not just in Ukraine, war is happing everywhere.
Israel and Palestine and countless other countries too.
War is happening everywhere.

Women, children and men dying every day.
Innocent people getting shot.
Hung or beheaded, it is scary but it is the truth.
Would you like to be in their shoes?
Knowing they might die, knowing that they might not see their families again.

Soldiers going into war, not knowing if they will see their friends or families alive.
In Iran, protesters dying for standing up to their controlling government.

## Aidan Hynes (11)
Tiree High School, Isle Of Tiree

# The Sorrow Of A Tree

I was mighty and tall with roots down to ore,
I would stand through the breeze,
I was a tree,
I could shelter,
I could grow,
I was the king of the wood.

Then they came,
They chopped me down,
They broke me up,
They threw me around a truck,
The screams of their weapons still haunt me,
I was pushed on a grinder,
All mushed up and pulped,
Now I am dead.

They moulded me,
They tore me,
Now I am full of a story,
But still sorry I couldn't fulfil my goal,
I never saw the light of snow.

That is my story,
I was broken,
Now I am at peace but still, I do not sleep,
For the pain of my sorrow,
I was a tree.

## Charlotte Vale (12)
Tiree High School, Isle Of Tiree

# I Don't Like Poetry

I don't like this,
I don't like poetry,
I'm sitting here at my desk wishing I am somewhere else.
But I guess I have to do this since my teacher signed us up,
I want to win,
I really do,
But I can't do this at all,
It's true,
I don't like this,
But maybe this is good I don't have a clue,
We have more to be worried about,
Other than poems,
Animals are dying,
People are dying,
There must be something we can do,
Other than sit and watch it happen,
But anyway,
I don't like poems,
Not at all,
But I tried,
And you should too.

**Zoe Maguire (12)**
Tiree High School, Isle Of Tiree

# Cyber Slander

Why me?
Why would you do that to me,
It made me sad and mad!

Why *me?*
I hope you don't do it again and hurt someone else too.
*You* made me feel devastated!

*Why* me?
How would you feel if someone did it to you,
Writing hurtful words for all your friends to view!

*Why me?*
You don't have to like me... the feeling is mutual,
You don't need to be my friend!

*But* if you don't have anything kind to say,
Then *silence* is golden!
As *slander* is really *unkind!*

## Iona MacDonald (11)
Tiree High School, Isle Of Tiree

# Annoyances

People eating with their mouth open
Constant *smack*, *smack*, *smack*
Makes me want to punch their face broken
Proper *smash*, *smash*, *smash*.

You're too loud, stop screaming
Shut up, shut up, I don't care
You're making me cry, tears streaming.

Don't make me do what you say
I'm tired, just let me sleep, let me lay.

Quit coughing in my face
You're disgusting, it's not funny
Move away, give yourself some space.

## Molly Knowles (14)
Tiree High School, Isle Of Tiree

# Spiders, Birds And Cats

Spiders are boring because no one
likes them
Most people are scared of them
and they do nothing but eat flies and bugs and insects.

Birds eat spiders and fly like flies,
they have nests in the trees and have different colours.
There are fifty billion birds in the world!

Cats eat birds and
chase spiders, they also
are the second most popular house pets with thirty million
cats in people's houses,
the lion and tiger are also
members of the cat family.

## Evie Meyer (12)
Tiree High School, Isle Of Tiree

# Football Is Life

It's a happy game
It's an angry game
Some people think it's all the same
Some people think it's just easy and
Just kicking a ball it's more than that and
Harder no matter big or small.

It doesn't really matter what you think
If you don't like football you stink.

It's a hard sport, you can injure yourself
And risk your life but only worry
About yourself.

Football is life.

**Lewis Gunn (13)**
Tiree High School, Isle Of Tiree

# Dunkin It!

Food is food, food is good, food is misunderstood, food is
the cure
Are doughnuts not food?
We waste
We don't taste
We starve
We die
Thirty to forty percent are loss
150 million would beg to be The Boss
We waste
There's no aftertaste
900 million daily gone
No going back
283s fighting
No aftertaste
We waste
We lose.

## Honey-Jane Romio (13)
Tiree High School, Isle Of Tiree

# Living

What is living right now?
Sadness
Depression
Anger
Hopelessness
Stress
Fear
Why do we fight?
What is money to us
Cold
Wet
Scared
Money forcing us out of our homes
The hope is slowly dying
Forty-six million wanting to live
What is living right now?

**Lucy Kennedy (11)**
Tiree High School, Isle Of Tiree

# Hatred

Hatred is awful
No matter the kind or circumstances
Past or present
For a reason or not.

We shouldn't make enemies or foes
We should focus on being friendly to everyone
Being friendly to everyone opens new opportunities
New doors, new people.

## Max MacKinnon (14)
Tiree High School, Isle Of Tiree

# Don't Smoke

Don't smoke
Smoke is a joke
It's bad for your throat
And it is gonna cost you a ten-pound note
So don't smoke
You stupid bloke.

**Maurice Wright (11)**
Tiree High School, Isle Of Tiree

# Shine Little Star

My little star is shinier than yours
I'm in the pool waiting for you.

You want to have a competition?
Okay
Be prepared
I won't forget!

When you lose, don't come begging
You chose your star
I don't care.

So one warning:

*Be prepared.*

## Yuri Silva (11)
Wayland Academy, Watton

# Environment!

Beautiful land it used to look,
But now it's just ruined and dead,
We need to forget about the things that we did,
And make it a safe and clean world.

**Nadia Lenartowicz (11)**
Wayland Academy, Watton

# Autumn Poem

A poem of mine,
Will send happy glitter down your spine,
Grab your wine,
For it's autumn time.

## Ryan Blockwell (11)

Wayland Academy, Watton

# Young Writers Information

We hope you have enjoyed reading this book – and that you will continue to in the coming years.

If you're the parent or family member of an enthusiastic poet or story writer, do visit our website www.youngwriters.co.uk/subscribe and sign up to receive news, competitions, writing challenges and tips, activities and much, much more! There's lots to keep budding writers motivated!

If you would like to order further copies of this book, or any of our other titles, then please give us a call or order via your online account.

Young Writers
Remus House
Coltsfoot Drive
Peterborough
PE2 9BF
(01733) 890066
info@youngwriters.co.uk

Join in the conversation!
Tips, news, giveaways and much more!

 YoungWritersUK    YoungWritersCW    youngwriterscw